Douglas I

Perseverance Island

Douglas Frazar

Perseverance Island

1st Edition | ISBN: 978-3-75234-144-7

Place of Publication: Frankfurt am Main, Germany

Year of Publication: 2020

Outlook Verlag GmbH, Germany.

Reproduction of the original.

PERSEVERANCE ISLAND.

BY Douglas Frazar

PREFACE.

In all works of the Robinson Crusoe type, the wreck is always near at hand, the powder dry and preserved, and the days for rafting the same ashore calm and pleasant. This unfortunate had no such accessories; and his story proves the limitless ingenuity and invention of man, and portrays the works and achievements of a castaway, who, thrown ashore almost literally naked upon a desert isle, is able by the use of his brains, the skill of his hands, and a practical knowledge of the common arts and sciences, to far surpass the achievements of all his predecessors, and to surround himself with implements of power and science utterly beyond the reach of his prototype, who had his wreck as a reservoir from which to draw his munitions.

THE MANUSCRIPT.

To the Person who shall find this Manuscript, Greeting,—

I hope that in the mercy of God these lines may come to the hands of some of my fellow-creatures, and that such action may be taken as may be deemed best to inform the world of my fate and that of my unfortunate comrades; if the finder will, therefore, cause the accompanying account to be published, he will confer a lasting benefit upon his humble servant,

Robinson Crusoe,

Otherwise called William Anderson.

Everybody must remember the setting out of the schooner "Good Luck" from the Liverpool docks, England, in the summer of 1865, with the advance guard of a colony to be established in the Southern Pacific, on one or more of its numerous islands to be selected; and from that day to this, the non-reception of any news of her from her day of sailing.

I am the only survivor of that ill-fated vessel, and record here, in hopes that the manuscript may reach the eyes of those interested, all the facts of the case, and pray that they will speedily send to my relief some vessel to take me home, and permit me once more to gaze upon the faces of my fellow-men before I die.

THE FINDING OF THE MANUSCRIPT.

SHOTTSVILLE, DELEFERO COUNTY, TEXAS,

April 1, 1877.

RETURNING to my home in the evening after a hard day's work on my quarter-section farm, I saw in the twilight an object dangling in the air, and apparently fast to a young walnut sapling. I approached it and found that it was a small balloon of about three feet in diameter, made, I should think, of some kind of delicate skins of beasts or birds sewed cunningly together. Attached in the place where the car should be, I found the manuscript herewith submitted, written on some kind of parchment, which, being taken home and read, I found of such startling interest that I have, although poor, ordered the same published at my expense in hopes that some action may be taken by those whom it may concern to move further in the matter. I further depose that the accompanying manuscript is the original one found by me attached to the balloon, and that it has never been tampered with or allowed to leave my possession till this moment. It can be examined, as well as the balloon, at any time, by any responsible person, by calling upon me.

[Signed] REUBEN STANLEY.

STATE OF TEXAS,

SHOTTSVILLE, DELEFERO COUNTY, S.S.

April 1, 1877.

Then personally appeared before me the said Reuben Stanley, to me well known, and made oath that the above deposition made by him is true.

[Signed] RICHARD HILLANDIER,

Justice of the Peace.

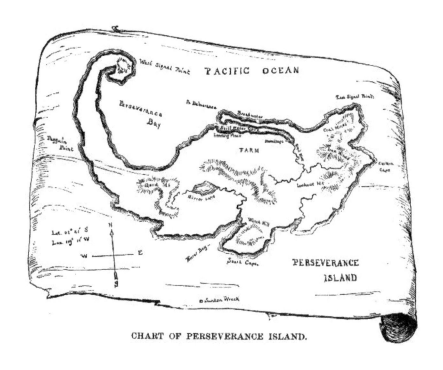

CHART OF PERSEVERANCE ISLAND.

CHAPTER I.

Boyhood and youth of the author. Sailor's life. The "Good Luck." South Pacific Island scheme. Loss of crew off Cape Horn.

I was born in the year 1833, in the State of Vermont, United States of America, and at an early age lost both parents by that fearful scourge, the small-pox. I was an only child, and upon the death of my parents, which happened when I was about six years of age, I was taken charge of by a friendly farmer of a neighboring town, who put me to school for several years in the winter, and at work upon the farm in the summer. I had no known relatives in the wide world, and often felt the bitter pangs of orphanhood. My master was not, however, unkind, and I grew up strong, robust, and with rather a retiring, quiet disposition, with a great love of mechanics and tools. Under all this quietness, however, lurked, I well knew myself, an unappeasable love of adventure and enterprise. I loved to lie in the open fields at night under the full moon; to explore swamps and brooks; and I soon learned to swim in the pond near by. At the age of fourteen I left my master, with his consent, and went to work in a neighboring machine-shop, where castings, etc., were made. I loved all manner of mechanical tools and instruments, and evidently had a taste in that direction. At the age of eighteen I became restless, and, having read during leisure hours many books of adventure and discovery, I took it into my silly head to become a sailor, and upon the inspiration of a moment I packed up my small bundle of clothes, and, bidding good-by to my workmates, started out on foot for Portsmouth, N. H. I arrived there and shipped as green hand in the schooner "Rosa Belle" for Boston, at which port we in due season arrived. From thence I shipped again before the mast in a large, square-rigged vessel for a voyage round the world. It is not my intention here to give a detailed account of my adventurous life till I joined the "Good Luck;" suffice it to say that during fourteen years at sea I passed through all the grades of boy, seaman, able seaman, boatswain, third mate, second mate, and first mate. It was after my discharge from a large clipper ship in Liverpool, lately arrived from China, in the latter capacity, that, having some few hundred dollars by me, I began to look about to see if I could not gain a livelihood in some easier way than by going to sea, being by this time heartily tired of the life, and for want of friends and relations with little chance of rising higher in the profession; it was at this time, I say, that this cursed project of the "Good Luck" was brought to my attention. As fate would have it, the schooner lay in the same dock with ourselves, and I became interested in her by hearing the talk upon the dock that she was bound to the South Pacific Islands to seek for pearls, sandal wood, tortoiseshell, etc., and to establish a colony of which the persons who were going out on this trip were the advance guard and projectors. I remember now, oh! how sadly, the Utopian ideas that were advanced, and although I, as a sailor in those seas, knew many of them to be false, yet imagination proclaimed them true. I could not resist the impulse to join my fortune to theirs. Having made up my mind, I called upon the chief movers in the matter and offered my services. It was first a question with them whether I could subscribe any money to the project, and secondly, what position I desired in the adventure?

I satisfied them upon the former, by stating that if I was pleased with their plans I could subscribe four hundred dollars in cash, and my services as a seaman and navigator in those seas. This seemed very satisfactory, and I was then asked, more pointedly, what position I demanded. I said that I should be satisfied with the position of chief officer, and second in command on board of the schooner, and fourth in command on the island as concerned the colony,—that is to say, if their plans suited me, which I demanded to know fully before signing any papers and bound myself by oath not to disclose if, after hearing and seeing everything, I declined to join them.

This straightforward course seemed to please the managers, and I was put in full possession of all their plans, and immediately after signed the papers.

It is sufficient for me to give an outline of this plan simply, which, through the act of God, came to naught, and left me, a second Robinson Crusoe, on my lonely island.

The company was formed of one hundred persons, who each put in one hundred pounds to make a general capital,—except a few like myself, who were allowed a full paid-up share for eighty pounds, on account of being of the advance guard, and wages for our services according to our station, with our proportionate part of the dividends to be hereafter made.

With this fund paid in, amounting to about nine thousand eight hundred pounds, the managing committee purchased the schooner "Good Luck." She was a fore-topsail schooner, of one hundred and fifty-four tons measurement, built in Bath, Maine, and about seven years old,—strong, well built, sharp, and with a flush deck fore and aft. She cost two thousand four hundred pounds. The remainder of the money was used in purchasing the following outfit for the scheme we were engaged in:—

Four breech-loading Armstrong cannon, nine pounders, four old-fashioned nine-pounders, twenty-five Sharpe's breech-loading rifles, and twenty-five navy Colt's revolvers, with plenty of ammunition for all. These, in conjunction with boarding-pikes, cutlasses, hand-grenades, and a howitzer for the launch, comprised our armament. The hold was stored with a little of everything generally taken on such adventures,—knives, hatchets, and calico for the natives, and seeds, canned meats, and appliances for pearl fishing, house-building, etc., for ourselves. To these were added a sawmill, an upright steam-engine, a turning-lathe, blacksmith tools, etc.

Our plan was to find an island uninhabited, that would form a good centre from which to prosecute our purpose of pearl gathering, and to there establish a colony, sending home the "Good Luck" for the rest of our companions and their families.

Ten of us were chosen as the advance guard (all but three being sailors), to make the first venture, establish the colony, load the schooner, leave part of our force upon the island selected, and the remainder to bring back the schooner to Liverpool. "Man proposes, but God disposes."

On July 31, 1865, we set sail upon this disastrous voyage, and from that day to this have I never seen the faces of civilized beings except those on board of the schooner, and not those for many months. Our captain was a fine, manly fellow, of about eight and thirty years of age, and we all liked him. Duty on board was of course different than it would have been in a common vessel; and although we had watches and regular discipline, each was familiar with the other, having, as we had, an equal stake in the adventure.

We had a tough time off Cape Horn, and, although the "Good Luck" behaved well, it was here that we met with our first misfortune. In stowing the jib, in a gale of wind, preparatory to laying-to, three men were swept overboard, and we never saw them more. This cast a damper upon the remaining seven, and was but a precursor of what was yet to happen. We rounded Cape Horn the first part of October, and, steering northwest, soon reached more pleasant weather. Our course was towards the group of islands, so well known in the South Pacific, called the Society Islands.

CHAPTER II.

Push forward for the Society Islands. Driven into Magellan Straits by stress of weather. Anchor in a land-locked bay. Search for fresh water. Attacked by savages. Serious injuries to Capt. Davis and one of the crew. Return to the schooner and make sail for the open ocean. Resolve to return to England. Finally lay our course for Easter Island.

WE had proceeded but a very short way towards the Society Islands when a terrific storm arose from the westward, driving us back upon the coast of South America. We lay to for many days, bending down before the blast, and drifting all the time rapidly to the southward and eastward; till one morning we discovered land broad off our lee beam, and, by a forenoon observation which the captain obtained, we found that we were off the western opening of the Straits of Magellan, and we soon put the schooner's head before the howling blast and ran in for shelter, rest, and repairs. We came up with the land very rapidly under easy sail, and passed the frowning cliffs and rocks on our port hand, not over a mile distant, as we knew we had plenty of water and to spare. After having passed the opening we hauled the schooner up on the port tack, heading her well up to the northward, intending to find some quiet land-locked cove where we could anchor and repair the damages—small in detail, but quite grave in the aggregate—that we had received in our buffeting of the last ten days.

About eight bells in the forenoon we found ourselves well inside the land, and with a smooth sea and a good fair working breeze, we kept the land well on the port beam and gradually crawled in toward it.

At about 4 P.M. we estimated that we were twenty miles inside the headlands, and having come to an arm of a bay trending well to the northward, we hauled the schooner sharp on a wind and steered into it; we discovered soon that it was about ten miles deep and thirty wide as near as we could judge; and as we came toward the head of the bay we found that we could run into a small inner bay of about three miles in area, with evidently smooth water and good anchorage. Into this inner bay or anchorage we quietly sailed and let go an anchor in six fathoms of water, and at a distance of about one mile from the shore.

When the sails were all properly furled, and everything put in "ship-shape and Bristol fashion," as the saying is amongst sailors, we had time to look about us; and the motion of the vessel having ceased, and the creaking of the masts and cordage, the flapping of the sails, and the usual noises of the sea, having come to an end, we were struck with the awful and sublime solitude of our surroundings. By this time the moon had risen, and by its light we saw the shadowy shapes of monstrous cliffs and miniature headlands covered with tangled forests of a species of pine, mirrored in the little bay in which we hung at anchor; but not one sound of life, no lights on shore, no cry of bird or beast, but the depressing, awful solitude of an unknown land; no noise except the graceful rise of the "Good Luck" to the miniature waves of the bay as she lay at anchor with twenty fathoms of chain out. We all spoke in whispers, so awe-striking was the scenery, and when we set the anchor watch and turned in it was unanimously conceded that we had little to fear in landing on the morrow either from natives or wild beasts.

Glad enough were we, after our long fight with the stormy ocean, to turn into our berths. It was chilly, although now past the middle of October, yet we saw no snow upon the ground, and the air had the smell of spring and verdure. This was easily accounted for when we remembered that in reality we were in the latter part of April as to seasons, and that we were no further south, than Great Britain is north, as concerns latitude. No doubt, also, the climate was favorably affected by this great arm of salt water penetrating the land. At any rate we had nothing to complain of on the score of ice and snow, which we should have found in plenty had we arrived a month or two earlier. Our captain had some very good traits, and was very systematic. For instance, he said that he would never allow a boat to leave the vessel to visit the shore, to be gone even an hour, without being properly rationed, and with flint, steel, and tinder, and also two large tin canisters filled with garden seeds. He had a hobby that it was our duty to plant seeds in all of the out-of-the-way places that we visited, for the good of those who might come after us. Carrying out these ideas, he had had our whaleboat on deck—whilst we were running by the land—righted and filled with the above-named articles, ready for use in the morning; that is to say, he had ordered to be put on board of her cooked rations for six days for four men, two breakers of fresh water, one bag of hard tack, a compass, two large tin canisters with water-tight screw-heads, filled with peas, beans, cucumber seeds, one hatchet, one knife, and a spare coil of rope.

The next morning, when we arose, there was a general desire to land upon the unknown coast, and we bethought ourselves of the plan of drawing lots to see who should stay on board and who go ashore, as the vessel would need the care of at least three hands, leaving four of us to go in the boat. Lots were drawn, and the privilege of going in the boat fell upon Captain Davis, two of the sailors, and myself. I was overjoyed at the opportunity of exploring this new world. Captain Davis told us to arm ourselves well with rifles and revolvers, and to be in readiness to start after breakfast, sharp.

No pleasanter party ever shoved off from a vessel's side than we on that pleasant October morning. We soon reached the shore, and, pulling up the boat upon the beach, were soon roaming here and there, stretching our legs and enjoying the novelty of our position. It was evident that the place was a complete solitude, and we doubted if any civilized persons had ever visited the shores of the bay before.

We wanted most of all things a supply of fresh water, and to this end we wandered somewhat apart and towards the upper part of the bay, concealed by overjetting cliffs, to see if there was not some stream or river flowing into it. After a little we heard a cry of delight from a comrade in advance, and hastening toward him found that after turning a short and abrupt point of rocks, a river of some considerable width lay before our eyes, evidently navigable with a small boat for some miles, but, as far as the eye could extend, no sign of any habitation. We ran gayly back to the boat, launched her, and soon pulled round the overhanging cliff that had concealed the presence of the river from us.

I should judge that we had pulled some five or six miles when we began to get hungry, and thought by the sun that it was about noon, and that we would land and eat our dinner. Up to this time we had found no side brook or spring entering the main river, and each turn was so enticing that we kept on passing bend after bend.

We landed upon a nice sandy beach, and soon had a pot boiling, and some clams, of which there were vast quantities in the sand, cooking upon hot stones. We made a capital meal, and after a good smoke took our oars again and went on up the river. Shall I ever forget the ending of that pleasant day? As we were chatting and passing a bend, and opening a new reach, in one moment of time our ears were filled with awful shrieks and shouts, and we had become the centre of a perfect shower of missiles from the cliff underneath the base of which we had just passed.

Our first instinct was to drop our oars and grasp the firearms, and a dropping, irregular fire into the bushes at the foot of the bend and towards the higher cliff towering above us brought to a sudden cessation the shower of stones with which we had been assailed, and with wild cries of fear, pain, and awe these untutored savages fled into the dense forest behind them.

I was amazed at the ease with which we had repelled them, until I bethought me that probably our firearms were the first they had ever heard. I wondered why we had not fired more, and quicker, and turning my eyes from their disappearing bodies, I saw, with horror, the cause. Captain Davis lay in the stern sheets of the boat with a large stone across both legs, dropped evidently from the cliff, which was some twenty or thirty feet above us, upon them. He had fainted away, or else was dead from some other wound, for he did not offer to stir or remove the stone. I glanced towards my other two comrades, and found, upon examination, one with a serious fracture of the left arm, which, however, did not prevent his holding on to his revolver in a most determined manner, and the other with only a few slight bruises. I beckoned him to come aft and help lift the stone off the captain's legs, we did so, and threw water in his face to revive him. We dared not imagine how bad his injuries were, and left him lying as we found him, after throwing overboard the stone, which undoubtedly would have gone through the bottom of the boat and sunk us, if it had not encountered the legs of the captain in its descent. As for our other comrade, we bound up his arm as best we could. I felt dizzy and weak, but did not suspect any serious injury. All that I have written was performed quickly, as sailors always act in an emergency. Bill Thompson and I soon got the boat's head pointed down stream, and the way we pulled for the ship was a sight to behold; pausing once in awhile to lift a hand and explode a revolver to keep the savages from attacking us again; but they had evidently had enough of it, for we saw no signs of them, and after a long and arduous pull we came to the ship's side, and sad was the news that we had for our comrades. We slung the boat and hoisted her on board, and I ordered the anchor to be weighed at once, and we set sail from this treacherous bay. It was found upon examination that one of the captain's legs was broken, evidently a compound fracture, and the other much bruised and inflamed. He was carried with care and affection to his stateroom, and I took charge of the deck. The sailor's arm was found to be a simple fracture, and we soon had it in splints and himself in his berth. After the schooner was fairly under way and heading out of the bay, I went below to my stateroom, and found that I had received several severe blows, but none that had drawn blood, except in the back of my head, where I found the hair under my cap bloody and matted together. This it was that had made me dizzy, although my excitement had been so great that I could not fix where the pain was till all was over. I washed myself, and went on deck again, to remain there during the night and run the schooner out into the open sea. What thoughts passed through my brain as the little vessel gallantly slipped along by the land, towards the ocean!—what in the world were we to do should Captain Davis die, and where were we to recruit, for during the long watches of that night it was agreed that we had become too short handed to prosecute our enterprise, and that the best thing that we could do would be to make our way back to England and start afresh; but after a long consultation, it was acknowledged that we were in no condition to face Cape Horn, and that we must get somewhere to recruit before we dare attempt the passage home. The captain, who had his senses perfectly, although suffering bodily pain, said "that we must make one of the easterly of the Society Islands before attempting to go home, and there recruit ourselves, overhaul the vessel, and by that time he should know what he was to expect of his own health, but feared that his injuries were beyond mortal aid." Towards morning the open sea appeared ahead, and at about eight bells, we issued from the mouth of Magellan Straits, and I laid the course of the schooner northwest, so as to hit Easter Island, or some of the islands further to the westward should the wind haul. At two bells in the forenoon we were bowling along on our course with everything set, and a fine working breeze from north-northeast, and a smooth sea. Of course we talked over the disastrous trip of the day before, and, as in all such cases, wondered why we did not do so and so, and why we were not more careful, etc., but to what good. The deed was done: our comrade with his broken arm, and our captain with his broken leg, were mute reminders of our folly and carelessness. My greatest fear at this time was that we should lose the captain, and that his duties would devolve upon me. He seemed throughout this day slightly better, but upon examination we found that we could not set his leg as we had the sailor's arm, and that, although he complained of little pain, his leg had a puffed and swollen appearance, and I feared the worst. I was somewhat in favor of changing the course and making a port on the South American coast; but the captain would not hear of it. He said "you can at least get to the Society Islands and land your cargo in some port under some flag where it will be safely kept till you return to England for a new crew. I shall not get well any sooner, if at all, on the South American coast than I shall in the Society Islands. We are bound by honor to push the adventure to its legitimate end, or as near it as possible." This and many other convincing things were uttered by him. "If my leg should have been amputated it should have been done before this; and it will be too late to do anything at Santiago as well as at Easter Island. You can still do a great deal towards making the adventure a success; perhaps you can even get volunteers enough in the islands to fill up your ranks, so as not to have to go back to England till you have your headquarters established and a cargo ready to ship back." And thus this sick and dying man cheered us on.

The end of the day found us with a still fresh working breeze headed for Easter Island.

CAPTAIN DAVIS WOUNDED.—PAGE 14.

CHAPTER III.

Captain Davis's condition. Only five men fit for duty. Terrific storm. The schooner thrown on her beam ends and dismasted. Loss of three more of the crew. Taking to the whale-boat. Foundering of the schooner "Good Luck." Death of Captain Davis. Storm again, running to the southward before the tempest. Strike upon a reef. The author cast on shore.

THE next fifteen or twenty days passed over us without anything material interfering with our advancement towards the islands.

During this time the change in the condition of Captain Davis had become worse; and we could all see that he was failing surely but rapidly; the sailor with the broken arm, on the other hand, was every day gaining strength and health, and bid fair to be soon amongst us again and at work. Bill Thompson and myself had fully recovered from the bruises and blows that we had received, and were in excellent health.

The duty at this time was rather exhaustive, as there were only five of us, including myself, fit for duty, and our turn at the wheel came about pretty often, as we, being so short-handed, had each to take our "trick." Our vessel was small, to be sure, and easily handled, but reduced, as we were, to five men, it was no boy's play to manage her.

In the first place, it needed a man at the helm night and day; then there was the cooking to be taken charge of; and at night the lookout man on the forecastle; these were three imperative duties which admitted of no change or neglect, and, divided amongst five persons, and including the watches at night, gave us plenty to do and to think of.

On November 5 we went about our usual duties in the morning, washing down the decks, and making everything snug and cleanly, as seamen like to see things. At noon I was able to get a good observation of the sun, which gave us lat. 40° 89′ 12″ S., and longitude by two forenoon observations by chronometer, 112° 5′ 54″ W. from Greenwich. The wind had for the last two weeks steadily hauled ahead, and we had been close-hauled and often unable to lay our course, hence I found the schooner much too far to the southward, but with her longitude well run down, and it was my purpose to decrease our latitude, even if we had to stand on the other tack to the northward and eastward. We were about fifteen hundred miles to the westward of the Straits of Magellan, which was not a bad run for a small vessel of the size of the

"Good Luck;" especially when it was to be remembered that we had also made several degrees (about ten) of northing, in latitude.

The afternoon shut down cloudy and threatening, and I hastened to the cabin to consult the barometer; I found no great change, but marked it with the side regulator, so as to be able to see if there was any sudden change within the next hour or two. At about eight bells (4 P. M.) the wind shifted suddenly to about N. N. W., and then died away and left us bobbing about in a heavy cross-sea, with dark, dirty weather to the northward and westward, but with little or no wind.

I examined the barometer again, and to my dismay saw that the mercury had fallen rapidly since my last visit. Everything about us showed that we were about to catch it, and although I knew that we were out of the track of typhoons and cyclones, still we were evidently about to experience a heavy gale of wind; the admonitions of nature were too evident and palpable to be misunderstood. I called all hands, and we went to work with a will to put the schooner in order for the coming blast.

We soon had the foretopsail lowered on the cap, close reefed, and then furled to the yard. We then took two reefs in the mainsail, and reefed and then stowed the foresail; got the bonnet off the jib, and the outer jib furled. Under this short sail we awaited the coming of the inevitable. First, the day grew darker, and was overcast with clouds of inky blackness; then came the mysterious sobbing and moaning of the ocean that all sailors have experienced; then the jerky and uneven motion of the schooner on the heavy swells for want of enough wind to keep her canvas full and herself steady.

Finally, towards evening, the pent-up storm came madly down upon us from the N. N. W., where it had been so long gathering its strength and forces. We laid the schooner's head to the westward and awaited the blast. Oh! if we only could have had wind enough to have gotten steerage-way upon her, so as to have luffed up into the howling blast, I might have been spared writing this narrative; but lying, as we were, almost dead upon the waste of water, we were compelled to receive the blast in all its strength, not being able to yield an atom to it. We had done all that men could do, except to await the result and trust in the mercy of God. I do not think that there was very much fear as to the result; there was a certain anxiety, however; but sailors never believe that wind or sea can hurt them till it does so. We expected to be struck hard, and to suffer some damage; but I think no one on board of that schooner had the slightest idea of the shock that we were about to receive. As the storm, or rather advance whirlwind, approached, we took our different stations and awaited the result. It came upon us with a crash, and in spite of all our care and skill the foretopmast went over the side, followed by the jibboom and maintopmast, as if the whole fabric had been made of paper, and the schooner was thrown violently upon her beam-ends. We lowered away the mainsail halyards, and, by cutting away the wreck to leeward, finally got her head before the wind, when she righted, and we dashed off before the tempest with nothing set but the jib, the mainsail having blown out of the bolt-ropes. Black night shut down upon us like a pall, and sheets of rain and spray fell upon us in torrents; thunder and lightning played about us, lighting up the decks one moment as bright as noonday, and the next leaving us in the most intense darkness, with a feeling about the eyes as if they had been burned up in their sockets. After the "Good Luck" once got started she did pretty well, scudding before it, but the forward sail was too small for the tremendous sea getting up astern of us; and we were in deadly peril of being pooped, and feared it each moment. We could set no square sail, everything forward above the foretop having been carried away; and we had no means of hoisting the foresail, even if we had dared to set it, as the peak-halyards had been carried away with the fall of the topmast, and we could not repair them; so all we could do was to fasten down the companion-way and trust to luck in letting her run before it under the jib. I thought that I had seen it blow before, but such a gale as this I never experienced; the voice of the tempest howled so through the rigging that you could not hear the faintest sound of the human voice in its loudest tones. I stood at the wheel, after helping to cut away the wreck, aiding the man at the helm through that long and awful night. We lashed ourselves to the rail and rudder-head; and well was it that we did so, for we were repeatedly pooped, and large masses of water came in over the stern, and rushed forward over the decks, that would have carried us to a watery grave if we had not been lashed to our post. My comrade Bill Thompson and I had no means of knowing whether the others forward had fared as well as we, or had been swept overboard by the repeated invasions of the sea.

Before we had been able to cut clear from the wreck we had received several severe blows from the timbers alongside, how severe I had no means of judging as yet, but my great fear was that we had started a butt or been seriously injured by these floating spars before we had been able to get rid of them.

About two bells (1 A. M.) as near as we could judge, the thunder and lightning ceased; and the puffs of wind were less and less violent, so that it was easy for us to feel confident that the strength of the gale had passed us. At eight bells (4 A. M.) there was a great difference both in the sea and wind; the former was no longer to be feared, and the latter was fast dying out. With what anxiety did we watch for the first light of day,—hours of agony unknown to those who have never led a sailor's life. As the gray of the morning began to come upon us, both wind and sea abated more and more, till in the full light of the morning we lay a dismantled wreck upon the waste of waters, with scarcely wind enough for a fair topsail breeze, and the seas momentarily going down.

My first care was to rush into the cabin, and to the locker, and pounce upon some food, and my next to carry some to my companion at the wheel. After this I looked around me to take in our situation. The foremast was gone near the head, the foreyard had evidently parted in the slings, and the foretopmast, topsail, and hamper, all gone together over the port bow.

Bill Thompson and I both strained our eyes for a view of some of our companions forward, but not a living soul met our gaze. I descended into the cabin, and found the captain and the sailor with the wounded arm doing as well as could be supposed after such a night of horrors. Captain Davis was evidently much weaker and much worse. I gave them an outline of the misfortunes that had overtaken us, and then went forward with a beating heart to the companion-way, threw it open, and passed into the forecastle and found it empty; not one soul left of three gallant fellows to tell the story of their swift destruction. The repeated poopings that we had received during the night must have swept them into the sea. I passed on deck, and thence aft. I noticed that the cook's galley was gone, and the bulwarks on the starboard side, and all the boats, except our whaleboat, which, although full of water, still remained pinned down to the deck by the lashings across her frame to the numerous ringbolts. As I walked aft, I could not but think that the schooner seemed low in the water; but I for the moment put it down to her changed appearance on account of the loss of her bulwarks. By this time the sun had risen and as beautiful and mild a day as one might desire to see burst upon us. I relieved Thompson at the wheel, and the wounded sailor soon took it with his one arm; the vessel scarcely moving through the water with the light air now stirring. I went below for the sounding-rod, and hastened to the well, as I knew we must have made much water during the storm, and I prayed to God that it might be no worse. I pulled out the pump-bucket and inserted the rod, it came back to the deck, marking at least FIVE FEET of water in the hold. I struggled one moment with my emotion, and then, turning to my companions, I said, "Get Captain Davis on deck; clear away the whaleboat; this vessel, curse her, is doomed. She will not float one hour; she has started a butt."

Amazement was depicted upon the faces of my companions; but, sailor-like, they hastened to obey my commands. We went into the cabin, and with infinite care and solicitude lifted the captain out of his berth and carried him to the deck. We then gathered round the whaleboat, relieved her from her slings and fastenings, tipped her over upon the deck, and got out all the water, and righted her, and then launched her over the starboard side through the broken bulwarks, and, putting her in charge of the broken-armed sailor, let her drop astern by her painter. We commenced at once rummaging for stores; and out of a mass of stuff brought on deck I ordered the following into the boat (the spritsail and oars were already lashed to the thwarts): Two half casks of fresh water, one bag of hard tack, one bag of uncooked salt junk, a fishing-line and hooks, a pair of blankets, some canned meats, a compass, charts and quadrant, a Nautical Almanac, Bowditch's Epitome, and a very valuable book of my own, a Compendium of Useful Arts and Sciences, a few pounds of tea and coffee, four tin canisters containing garden-seed, matches, two rifles and four revolvers, and ammunition for the same; this, with the usual clothing of the men, was as much as I dared load the boat with; and, pulling her up alongside, we lowered the captain on board on a mattress, and proceeded to stow away the articles I have enumerated in as good order as possible. We stepped the spritsail forward and unlashed the oars, and got the steering oar out aft through the becket made for that purpose. I feasted my eyes upon the treasures round about me, but had sense enough not to allow the boat to be overloaded with trash, so as to swamp us in the first gale of wind. Having got everything on board, and carefully noted the day of the month, November 6th, in the Nautical Almanac, we cast off from the unlucky "Good Luck," and set our sail to keep near her till her final destruction took place, which to our practised eyes could not long be postponed, as she was evidently in the throes of death. We found that she was making so little headway on account of the light breeze, and from having settled so deep in the water, that we took in our sail and lay to upon our oars at a safe distance and watched her.

LAUNCHING THE WHALE BOAT.—PAGE 26.

Could anything be more miserable than our condition? Four unfortunate men, two of whom were crippled, one probably to the death, cast on the open ocean in an open boat, at least a thousand miles from any known land.

I thought of all the open-boat exposures of which I had ever read; of Lieutenant Bligh and the "Bounty," and others equally startling. I shuddered when I thought what our fate might be. I ran through, in my mind, the rapid events that had followed each other since our departure from England, and the unexplainable series of fatalities that had robbed us of our comrades till we remained only the little group now seated in this frail boat. In what direction should we steer? what was to be our fate? what had God still in store for us in the shape of misfortune and horror? It seemed as if the bitter cup had been full to overflowing, and that we had drained it to the very dregs. I was awakened from my day-dream by the voices of my comrades, who drew my attention, without speech, by pointing to the doomed vessel. We lifted Captain Davis in our arms, and with fixed eyes and set teeth saw the misnamed schooner drive her bows under the water, and then shortly after, majestically raising her forefoot high in air, sink down grandly into the abyss of ocean, leaving us poor unfortunates adrift upon its treacherous bosom.

After we had seen the last of the schooner we gathered together for consultation as to our course. It was demonstrated by the chart that we were much nearer to Easter Island than to any other land, say some eight hundred miles distant by projection. But, on the other hand, the wind hung persistently from the northward and placed us to leeward of our port. It was too far to think of standing back to the South American coast, and we felt that we must keep a northwesterly course, and if the wind headed us off from Easter Island, that we could at least fetch some of the more westerly of the Society Group.

Having decided upon this, we set our foresail and laid our course about W. by N., which was as high as the wind would allow us to lie. The day was pleasant and the wind light, and the sea quiet. I inaugurated at once a system of daily allowance, and for this first day we were to issue no rations, we all having had at least, although coarse and interrupted, one meal and plenty of water, before leaving the schooner. The days were growing perceptibly longer and warmer, and we ran all that afternoon quietly along over quite a smooth sea, making good headway to the westward, but little northing, which I was so anxious to make. As the sun went down Captain Davis, although very weak, called us all aft around him and, in a faint voice on the lonely ocean, from memory repeated for us all the Lord's Prayer; the loneliness of our situation and the solemnity of the occasion remain vividly in my mind to this day. We all saw that we must soon lose our captain, but no one dared to say as much to his neighbor; we could plainly see that his hours were few, and that the motion and exposure of the boat could not be endured by him much longer. After the sun went down I took the steering oar aft, and telling the men to lie down and get all the rest they could, I kept the boat on her course and seated myself near the captain, stretched on his mattress at my feet. At about ten o'clock, as near as I could judge, after a long and absolute silence, I heard Captain Davis utter my name. I bent down towards him, and he said, "Do not be shocked. I am soon, very soon, about to depart, the sands of life have almost run out, and I am weary and want to be at rest in the Haven of Repose. If you ever get back to England, tell them that I did my duty faithfully. I, as you know, have no wife or child to mourn for me, but I want you all to remember me as a just captain, with all my faults. I have no fear of being buried in the sea; God can find me anywhere at the great day, when we shall all be mustered on the quarter-deck for inspection, and, if worthy, promotion. If you are driven out of your course, keep to the westward still, and you will eventually find land. Say a prayer or two over my body when you commit me to the deep; and now wake up the men and let me say good-by to them, for I am going fast." I called up the men, and the two poor fellows came aft and shook the hand of our captain in sore distress; and we sat watching, unwilling to sleep or break the silence of that solemn moment. In about an hour Captain Davis opened his eyes, that had been closed, raised his arm slowly to his head, touched an imaginary hat, and said, "Come on board to report for duty, Sir,"—and passed away like a child dropping to sleep. We covered the body with our spare clothing, and each sat in sad reflection. Bill Thompson soon after relieved me at the oar, and I laid down in the forward part of the boat and tried to sleep; and such was exhausted nature that, in spite of our unfortunate condition, I soon dropped off. I was awakened early in the morning by a slight call from Bill, and sat up in the boat, rather bewildered for a moment, till I saw the outline of the body in the stern sheets, and then everything flashed back to my memory. I have little doubt but what that sleep saved me for the purposes that God has preserved me for to this day. It was thought best to dispose of the body before the full breaking of the day, and we for that purpose gathered around the remains, and, in compliance with the dead man's request, I recited the Lord's Prayer, and we committed the body to the deep. This event produced a new shock to our already overstrained systems, and we looked sadly enough upon each other with almost vacant eyes. We as yet were blessed with pleasant weather, and, although we were not heading up to our course, we were making westing quite fast. This day, November 7th, we passed without any remarkable event. As there were now only three of us left we found plenty of room in the boat to lie down at our ease, and it only took one of us to steer and look after the boat. We rearranged everything, and stowed all our articles in convenient places. So far, we had seen no signs of vessel or land, and we passed the day in sleeping and refreshing ourselves for whatever the future might have in store for us. The night was quiet and the stars shone down upon us with their silvery light, and we used them to keep our course by, having no light to see the compass in the night-time. Towards eight o'clock in the morning of the 8th the weather began to change, and large clouds to gather in the northern horizon; it was at this time that we made another discovery, and that was that one of the breakers of water had leaked out quietly till there was scarcely enough in it for our rations for that morning; this was caused by its not having been used for some time before we filled it on board of the ship. This discovery caused us great uneasiness, and although the breaker had evidently ceased leaking now, having swollen with the water placed in it, it was no longer useful, as we had no water to replace that which was lost. The weather to windward caused me great disquietude, and I was sadly afraid, in case of a blow, that my Nautical Almanac and Epitome and Compendium would be destroyed, either by rain or seas that we might ship. I bethought me, therefore, of copying off the declination of the sun for a few days, and the tables that I might want to use, on a spare leaf of the Epitome, and take out the head of the now useless breaker and enclose all the books and charts in it and head it up. This was accordingly done. We started the hoops, took out the head, put the books and charts in, carefully wrapped up in a piece of blanket, and replaced the head and closed up the bung-hole. I felt relieved after this, as I looked upon the preservation of my books as of the utmost importance in our future navigation, and I could think of no greater loss to people in our condition than to have them lost or destroyed. It was with infinite satisfaction that I saw them thus safely preserved from the water till I could again take them out in good weather and examine and copy from them.

Whilst we had been busy at this task the weather to windward was fast becoming bad and threatening. I dealt out a fair ration of hard tack and canned meat to my two comrades, and then ordered them to take the sprit out of the foresail, and bring the peak down to the foot of the mast, and lash it to the inner leach of the sail, and fasten what was before the after leach to the foot; so as to make a sort of double leg-of-mutton sail, with the body low down and along the boom. We labored with a will at our work, for the freshening breeze was fast coming down upon us, and at twelve o'clock, as I judge, we were plunging along quite well for so small a boat, in about half a gale of wind, which allowed us to head up as high as N. N. W. The sea, however, was getting up fast, and I foresaw that unless it moderated we should have to bear away and run before it. As I feared, we now commenced to take in considerable water, which, although not in dangerous quantities, gave us work to do in the shape of bailing with the empty meat cans, whilst the attention of one was needed without remission at the steering oar and sheet. We were, thank God, blessed with that best of seaboats, a Nantucket whaleboat; and although she was low in the water, she was also buoyant, and rode the waves better than could be expected of any other craft of her size. I felt, too, that we could at any time make easy weather of it by scudding or running before the wind, for which she was admirably fitted, being sharp at both ends, and therefore in no danger of being pooped; but this was the last thing that I desired to do, as it would take us from our course towards the islands and far to the southward, as such a boat would make rapid way before the wind, with even this small sail.

At about two o'clock the wind hauled more to the westward and headed us off to the southward. At three o'clock we had broken off to S. W., and the wind increasing, and the sea getting up fast, so fast that I already had to let the boat go very free before it, to keep her from being swamped.

At sundown the gale had greatly increased, and I found that to preserve us, and on account of the steady change of the wind, that I was compelled to steer about S. by W., and to allow ourselves to run before the tempest. As the darkness set down upon us like a pall, I gave ourselves up as lost. I clung to the steering-oar and guided the boat before the wind; the only clew that was given me how to steer was the angry roar of the combing billows astern and the rush of the wind by the side of my face: by these two senses of hearing and feeling, I was enabled to tell when the boat was about to broach to, which would have been destruction, and how to steer so as to keep her before the wind. The darkness was the darkness of the ocean in a storm, and torrents of rain and spray flew over us. I was unable to see an atom of even the sail ahead of me in the boat. And thus we plunged on, into the inky darkness, followed by the angry roar of the disappointed waves that we left astern. We were moving with frightful rapidity through the water; but in what direction I had no means of knowing.

I clung to the steering-oar, and my companions to their bailers; how many hours we thus rushed along I know not. I had become hardened to the situation, and the angry roar astern had become a familiar noise in my ears. I commenced to people the darkness with vessels, islands, sunlight, and music; I had long ceased to care what fate might have in store for me; I felt that the night must be nearly passed, and wondered whether we should survive to see the daylight. I dreamed, and became semi-unconscious, but still guided the boat onward before the wind.

I felt that nature could not be sustained much longer, and that in a few hours I must succumb. My comrades pottered round at my feet, their efforts to bail becoming more and more feeble. I was in this reckless, half-dazed state when, without one moment's warning, I was thrown with a crash into the forward end of the boat, and in another instant surrounded by pieces of the boat and floating débris. I found myself hurled rapidly forward by an incoming wave, and rolled over and over some hard substance; the next instant the retreating wave found me clinging to a mass of what was evidently land of some kind, and the sea already had a faint, distant sound to my ears. The next incoming wave dashed over some evident obstacle between me and it, and I clung to the object at which I had first clutched, ready to receive it. I was buried beneath it, but managed to keep my hold, and, as it retreated, the noise again became fainter, and it flashed over me that, by the first wave, I had been washed over some reef or barrier between the open ocean and where I now hung, and that each wave was broken by this barrier before reaching me.

Before the next wave came I had gained my feet, and felt that I was standing upon rocky ground, and clutching masses of rock-weed in each hand. I was again buried, but hung on with desperation till the wave had retired. Evidently I had been washed over the reef; but what was to leeward of me. By a sailor's instinct I knew that it was smooth water, and that I had at least a rocky barrier between me and the raging ocean outside. Every wave did not submerge me, but most of them did, and I felt that it was only a question of a few moments more how long I could hold on before trusting myself to swimming to leeward. O for some knowledge of what lay behind me. One flash of lightning, one speck of God's blessed daylight!

Was there land behind me? or should I let go my last hold upon life when I unclasped my hands from the rock-weed that they held to? My brain worked with lightning-like rapidity. I knew that I must not hang on to this reef, submerged every few moments, till all my strength was gone, so that I could not swim; this was to seek certain death; whereas, in letting go and swimming to leeward I had one chance to be saved. *If* there was land, it no doubt could be easily approached on account of the sea being stopped by the barrier to which I now clung. On the other hand, if the land to which I now hung was the only land, and the pitiless sea alone to leeward, then God have mercy upon my soul! I must do something. Although used to swimming and diving, I could not stand this submersion much longer, and my arms were fast giving out; therefore, when the next wave came, I let go my hold, and crying out, in my despair, "Oh, help me, Lord!" allowed myself to be carried away with it. In a moment I felt that my conjectures about smooth water had been correct. I swam without difficulty, in comparatively smooth water, encumbered only by my clothes. Should I find land before me? Oh, for light! Hark! did I hear the break of water upon land before me? and so near. Down went my feet, and I found myself standing in water not up to my armpits. The revulsion was terrible. I fell into the water, and scrambling, fighting, fainting, plunged forward till I found myself safe on shore and at some distance from the water, when I fell down unconscious on the sand.

CHAPTER IV.

Return to consciousness. Seek for my comrades. Commence a calendar, and take inventory of my effects.

How long I lay unconscious where I had scrambled and fallen down I shall never know, but when I awoke and stared around me, I found that it was broad daylight, and, by the sun, at least eleven or twelve o'clock in the day. I gazed around me and tried to collect my thoughts, and the horrors of the preceding night came slowly back to my memory. I arose and stretched my limbs, and with the exception of some stiffness in my joints, and bruises that were not of a serious nature, I found myself all right. I fell upon my knees and devoutly thanked God for my deliverance, and then arose and looked around me. I found myself standing on a smooth, sandy beach, which, by the sun, evidently ran nearly, if not quite, east and west; a narrow strip of water not more than a short quarter of a mile separated me from the reef over which I had evidently been swept the previous night. To my right hand, as I stood facing the north, ran a level beach of a mile or so in extent, ending in an elevation and hills at the extreme end, faced, its entire length, as far as I could see, by this natural breakwater or reef in front of me. To the left I discerned an opening to the sea about one mile distant; and beyond, low land extending for several miles, and ending in a promontory of some elevation. Turning about, I saw behind me, running down almost to the sandy beach, a grove of trees, with many of which I was familiar, and wooded higher land in the background.

My nautical knowledge told that there was no known land in this part of the world. Where was I? Where were my companions in the boat? Was the island inhabited by savages? Had I been saved to become their prey? All these questions rushed through my mind, but were unanswerable. I began to feel faint and sick with thirst, hunger, and fatigue, and devoured with an unappeasable curiosity to know the fate of my comrades; and to this end, I stripped off my clothing and waded into the water towards the reef over which I had so providentially been cast. I found the water shallow and with a pure, sandy bottom, and had only to swim a few rods to regain my feet again, and be able to reach the breakwater. With what intense excitement, fierce but restrained, I climbed the rocks, and gazed upon the open sea, you who have never been cast away, from home, kindred, and society can never know. I looked about me upon the rocks, and at the treacherous sea, now as smooth and smiling as a sleeping infant. In vain did I search for any traces of my comrades.

Not a sign of them was to be seen. Now that the storm had gone down, this breakwater of rocks stood several feet above the sea, irregular in width and height. By aligning myself on the place on shore where I had landed, and whence I had come, I felt sure that I must be near the spot where the boat had struck. I passed a little farther to the right, and came upon the scene of my disaster. Upon the rocks I found small portions of the boat, broken to atoms not larger than my hand, but no friend, no comrade, no living soul to cheer my despair. I saw in a very few minutes that if they had not been swept over the reef at the very first sea, as I had been, they had inevitably been washed back again into the ocean, dashed amongst the rocks, and sucked in by the undertow, never more to be seen by man. A very few moments' examination convinced me that such must have been the case. But one single chance remained, and that was, if they were swept over the reef as I was, if alive, their tracks would show on the sand of the shore behind me. I did not have the slightest faith in this, but saved it in my mind to be proved when I returned to the shore. Striving to put the horror of my position far from me, and trying to see if there was anything to be saved that could be useful to me in my miserable condition, I began to look about me in the crevices of the rocks for any small article that might have escaped the maw of the ocean. In about an hour's search I had gathered the following together, which was every atom that seemed to remain of the boat and her appurtenances,—the remainder had evidently been ground into powder against the rocks, and hurled back with the retiring waves into the insatiable ocean: One piece of boat-planking, about nine feet long and ten inches wide, which I preserved on account of its containing several nails which had bolted it to the keelson; one tin meat-can that we had used as a bailer, somewhat bent, which I found securely jammed in a crevice of the rock; one canister of preserved meat, thrown by the sea into a sort of natural cavity or pocket in the rocks; and last, the most important of all, the boat's anchor and rope cable, which had washed across the reef and hung with the end in the quiet waters of the inner bay. I grasped it and coiled it up, following it to the outer side of the reef, whence I pulled up the anchor, and found myself in possession of it and some twenty fathoms of good inch-and-three-quarter manilla rope. This constituted all my earthly fortunes, and, placing the anchor and rope and the empty meat canister and the full one upon the piece of boat-planking, which just barely supported them when submerged in the water, I thrust them carefully before me towards the other shore, and, getting too deep to wade, I guided them with one hand and pushed them before me till, again touching bottom with my feet, I soon had them on land, safe and sound, at the place where I had first landed, and beyond the reach of the sea.

As soon as these were secured, I started off to the left to examine the pure white sand to see if any human foot had come on shore but my own; but, alas, there was no sign. Turning, when I had reached a distance beyond which it would have been useless to look, I came back and made a similar exploration to the right. As I advanced I saw something black rolling quietly up and down the beach with each miniature wave. For one instant I mistook it for the body of one of my comrades; the next I knew it for one of the breakers that had been in the boat. I rushed into the sea and grasped it, its light weight told me at once that it was the one containing my charts, books, Epitome, and Nautical Almanac, that its very lightness had preserved it and allowed it to be cast over the reef at the very first sea, instead of being crushed, as the one full of water evidently had been, with the boat. With gratitude to God for even this slight mercy and solace, I dragged the cask well towards the land and beyond all danger of the sea.

Having made sure that there was nothing else to be saved, I came back to my first landing-place, sat down fainter than ever, but managed to get on my clothes, and with one of the rusty nails from the boat's plank to scratch upon a large stone near by, "November 9, 1865," after which I forced open the top of the canister of preserved meats, by means of the same nail and a small pebble, taking care not to cut the whole top quite out, but to leave it hanging by a kind of hinge. By punching hole after hole around the periphery of the canister with the point of the nail, close together, I soon had it off except in one portion purposely preserved. Pressing this cover back, I took a draught of what to me, in my state, might be called nectar, for it was both food and water, but which was in reality simply beef soup.

After this refreshing draught, I lay myself down upon the bank and gave myself up to meditation. After reclining upon the ground about half an hour, my eyes became fixed upon an object slowly approaching me from the right hand, and evidently going out of the narrow inlet in front of me with the tide, which was then at ebb. I rubbed my eyes, and thought I recognized an article belonging to the boat. I took off my clothes again and entered the water, and soon had hold of one of the large red powder-canisters, which had been filled with seeds and stored in the boat when we entered Magellan Straits. I eagerly seized upon my prize and brought it safely to shore, and found that it had been preserved perfectly water-tight by the screw in the top, through which hole the seeds had been dropped into it and then closed. I carried this canister to my former seat and sat myself down with all my worldly goods about me. I made mentally the following inventory of effects:—

On my person I had the following: I had lost my hat in the gale, and the remainder of my clothing consisted of one pair of coarse shoes, one pair of woollen stockings, one pair of flannel drawers, one pair of cheap woollen trousers, one flannel undershirt, one blue flannel shirt, one silk necktie. On the ground before me: one empty tin canister that we had used as a bailer, one empty tin canister that had lately contained the beef soup, one large tin canister, filled with garden seeds, one anchor of about forty pounds weight, and twenty fathoms of line, one piece of boat-planking with several nails, and the empty breaker, containing, as I knew by memory, one Bowditch's Epitome, one Nautical Almanac, one large book, entitled, "Compendium of Useful Arts and Sciences," and one chart of the South Pacific Ocean. In the pocket of my trousers I found one piece of plug tobacco, a small piece of twine, a hair comb, and clay pipe. My knife, for which I would have given so much, had either been laid down in the boat or since lost; it was, at any rate, gone, and I mourned for it.

My various duties in collecting these things about me; my former fatigue and depression, aided by the food I had swallowed, soon brought me to a state of drowsiness; and as the sun was now fast declining, I drew myself further upon the island and under a sort of cedar-tree,—the thick and low boughs of which formed a covering for my body from the dews,—and gathering my household goods about me, I, after meekly resigning myself to my fate and commending myself to God, lay quietly down and fell to sleep with the setting sun.

CHAPTER V.

Attempt to make a fire. Distil salt water. First meal. Reflections. Hat-making. Repose.

I SLEPT all night soundly in spite of the cool air and the novelty of my situation. When I awoke, the sun was about two hours high, and I came out from under my cedar-tree feeling quite refreshed, with the exception of an intolerable thirst. The want of water had troubled me on the preceding day, and it flashed across my mind, What shall I do if I find no fresh water?—what shall I do if I find no fresh water?—and this refrain kept now running through my head, accompanied with another tune, What will you do for fire?—what will you do for fire? These two melodies filled my ears without cessation. I arose from my seat on the bank, and proceeded to the sea in front of me, and washed my face and combed out my hair. I then fell upon my knees and invoked the assistance of Divine Providence in my distress. Having ended these duties I began to look about me for water,—water.

Should I start off at a venture and run the chance of finding water, failing in which I should perish, or should I at once begin to work with the brains that God had given me, to procure in a scientific manner that which Nature had refused? If, thought I, I start off and use up all my strength in a vain search, I can then but lay down and die; whilst on the other hand, by commencing now whilst I am comparatively fresh, to try and overcome this obstacle, I have two chances of life: for, failing here, I can as a last resort push forward into the island till I find water or lie down and die for want of it. Having thus firmly made up my mind, I began to think. To procure water I must first make fire. How should I do it? Matches I had none; flint, steel, or tinder I was without, and no means of procuring them. I *must* find steel, flint, and tinder, but where? how? My eyes fell upon the anchor, and that gave me an idea, but I knew that the iron of which it was composed was too soft and rusty to be of use for my purpose. I bethought me of the nails in the planking, but upon examination they also were too soft.

An inspiration struck me. I drew off one of my shoes, and by means of one of the larger nails and a pebble soon had one of the heels off, displaying a row of nails that I hoped were hard enough for my purpose. I pounded one of the most likely looking ones out of the leather, and found it quite hard and polished. I ran towards the line of pebbles that the sea had for ages cast up, and looked for a flinty stone to strike my nail upon. I tried several, but could get no spark. I began to despair. I had in boyhood thrown large stones together in the night time on purpose to see the sparks fly, but I was well aware that, obtained in this manner, they would be too weak to ignite any tinder, and my only salvation was in my shoe nail and a flint, or at least a flinty stone. I sought and sought, and tried and tried, without the slightest success. The sweat began to drop from my brow in great beads of excitement; finally I edged more towards the upper part of the beach and towards a small cluster of rocks further inland, whose base was also surrounded by small pebbles. I had almost given up hope, when, pushing the pebbles to one side, I turned up to the light one of a dirty yellow color that I was convinced was a veritable piece of flint. I seized upon it and wiped it upon my clothes, for it was damp, and felt convinced that it was genuine flint. I had to lay it in the sun to dry before I could prove it, and you can little know the agony that I endured in that short interval. At last the flint was dry, and, taking it in my hand, I struck it against the nail. Eureka! Eureka! A faint but perfect spark shone for an instant in the open air. I rushed back with my prize to my cedar-tree, and placing the nail and flint where I could easily find them, I plunged into the grove to look for tinder. I took within half an hour a hundred different substances in my hand to examine them and see if they would serve my purpose. Walking on, I came to a little open field with a short, sour grass, and it was here that I hoped to find my prize. Do you ask what I was looking for? I was looking for one of those dried-up balls, that, as boys, we used to burst open and see the dust fly, that we called nigger-balls. Moving along I came upon a plant that is sometimes used to make pickles of, and I knew that the pod contained a soft silky substance something like cotton. I seized upon this and pulled off an old last year's pod, and found the substance I was in search of. I did not know whether it would do for tinder or not, but I hoped so. I ran about the field looking to the right and the left, and as I was about to give the search up, right under my nose I espied a large nigger-ball. I fastened upon it and posted back to my bank near the cedar-tree. The time for the final test had come. Now to the supreme trial.

I burst open the nigger-ball and extracted a small quantity of the dark, dust-like powder that it contained, and laid it carefully upon a small, smooth stone. I then extracted some of the cotton-like fibre from my milkweed pod, and picked it carefully apart into minute atoms with my fingers, and mixed it into the dust before me on the stone. I gathered together minute dry twigs and leaves all ready to place upon the tinder should I be able to ignite it. I leaned over my tinder, and with the shoe nail grasped carefully and firmly in the left hand I placed it near to it, and with the right hand containing the flint struck it a smart blow. The first spark missed the tinder entirely. I moved my hand slightly, and the next stroke sent a fine spark into the very centre of the pile, and in one moment it was ignited, and a little snake of fire began to run in and out of the tinder. I blew carefully upon this and put little pieces of wood in the right places, petted and worked upon it until, with a careful but increasing blast, it burst into flame. I piled on wood and sticks till I felt sure of the result, and then commenced dancing and singing round about the flame, till in my weakness and excitement I fell down in a dead faint. I opened my eyes again to see my fire burning cheerily away as if it was the most natural thing in the world.

STRIKING FIRE WITH FLINT AND STEEL.—Page 48.

Now for water! water! I seized upon the canister of garden seeds, which was an old powder canister formerly, and would contain, I should say, a gallon of water, and poured out the seeds through the screw hole in the top upon a large flat stone, and covered them with a few leaves. Weak as I then was, I recognized beans, wheat, rice, corn, cucumbers, &c. I took the empty canister to the sea and washed it carefully out and brought it back filled with salt water, and placed it upon my fire, which was now burning splendidly. I rushed again to the seashore and picked up several long pieces of kelp, which we boys used to call devil's apron, and which I knew were long, hollow tubes that would suit my purpose admirably. With the small twine in my pocket, and a piece of my flannel shirt and various leaves, I bound one of these long tubes of kelp to the screw hole of the canister on the fire, and supported it clear of the flames by means of crotched sticks, which I tore from trees near by, and also built a wall round about the fire, to confine it more, made out of stones, upon which I rested the opposite edges of the canister. I led this tube of kelp, which was at least ten feet long, gradually down hill towards the ocean, and, digging a long furrow in the sand, I filled it with wet kelp and seaweed, placed my tube therein, and covered it up again with sand; at the orifice I dug quite a deep hole, and set one of the empty meat-cans under it to catch the dropping water that I knew must appear as soon as my powder canister commenced to boil. I took the bailer and rushed to the ocean, and saturated, by repeated trips, the sand under which my tube was buried. By this time my thirst was fearful, and having heard that bathing is sometimes useful in such circumstances, I dragged off my clothes, and, too weak to swim, I lay down in the cool water at full length upon the sandy bottom, within view of my fire and condenser. Anxious as I was, I knew that I must sustain my strength, and I could think of no better method than this. The cool sea water revived me greatly, more than I could have believed possible, and, fearing to stay in too long, I tottered ashore and to my little well. Water! water! There it was dribbling out of the tube of kelp into the meat-can—already an inch or two had collected. Although tasting badly of the salt kelp tube through which it had passed, you can little know the rapture with which I swallowed it and thanked God. In a few moments more I had enough for another swallow, and of a much better quality, less brackish, and by quietly waiting I soon had two or three inches of quite good water, brackish to be sure, but pure enough to support life and to course like quicksilver through my veins and give me a new lease of life. Suffice it to say that, by renewing my canister on the fire, I had in a few hours both the meat-cans full of water, and my craving thirst entirely quenched. Brains had won. I had both fire and water—two of the four elements—at my command. As soon as my thirst was appeased I commenced to feel the pangs of hunger, but this gave me little disquietude, for I had not been digging in the sand without observing that there were plenty of clams on every side of me, and with a short stick I soon had as many as I wanted on the surface, and from thence to the hot stones of my fire, where I covered them with wet seaweed and allowed them to roast. Whilst this was going on I strayed away to the left a short distance, where I had seen many gulls gathered together, and sure enough, as I suspected, I found the crevices of the rocks full of eggs. I took upon myself, as proprietor of the island, to abstract some dozen of them, and taking the large canister and rinsing it out with a very little of the precious fresh water, I poured the remainder into it from the meat-can, and started with the latter to the sea, and returned with it filled with sea water, which I placed upon my fire, and dropped into it half a dozen of my new-found eggs, which soon commenced to boil right merrily. By this time my clams were baked or roasted, and I sat down to my first meal, consisting of boiled eggs, baked clams, and fresh water, with a thankful and even a cheerful heart; for had I not overcome impossibilities almost, and made sure of the two great wants of humanity, fire and water, which meant food, life, everything?

Nature being satisfied, I began to think of the horror of my situation, the only survivor of a company of gallant fellows that had left England in such good spirits only a few months ago. Here was I, a poor Robinson Crusoe, alone and desolate on an unknown island. I tried to penetrate the dark future and discover what fate still held in store for me. By this time the day had passed into afternoon, and I felt the necessity of preparing for the coming night. My great fear was that the island was inhabited by savages, and if so I had preserved my life to little purpose, for I should, upon being discovered, probably be killed at once, or else be made to drag out a miserable existence as their slave, or be kept a captive by them for the term of my natural life.

I glanced about me and saw that the island was fair to look upon, and evidently of considerable extent. I desired to explore it, but prudence and fear restrained me. My first care was to get some covering for my head; the rays of the sun, although not oppressive, were uncomfortable. I passed again through the grove of cedars and into the open field, and looked about for something to make a hat of, but found nothing then to suit me. I returned to the seaside again, and what would do for the purpose struck my eye at once, namely, a sort of saltwater rushes which grew out of the sand in large quantities, not far from me to the right, similar to what we used to call at home sedge. I gathered sufficient of the riper and less green leaves and stalks for my purpose, and commenced to lay them up into what sailors call five-strand sennit, and what young ladies would call five-strand braiding. I soon had several yards of this material laid up, and found it quite well suited for my purpose. When I had what I deemed sufficient I took the nail I had before used to open the meat-can with, and which I kept in my pocket, and commenced to bring its end to a sharp point by grinding it upon a soft pebble that lay beside me, and having brought it to a point I went to work and unlaid about a fathom of my manilla rope, and, taking the edge of a clam-shell, sawed off one of the strands, and from that I selected a few threads, which I laid up again into a good strong twine. I then commenced at the crown of my straw hat, and by turning the sennit round upon itself I soon had that part completed, for as I passed once round, I, with the sharp nail as a pricker, forced holes through each part at distances of every two or three inches of the circumference, and passed my manilla twine through, knotted it, and cut it off with the edge of my clam-shell. In this way, in an hour or two I had quite a good straw hat with a large wide brim, and, although hastily tacked together instead of being sewed, it answered my purpose admirably. My hand being now in, I made, in the same manner and of the same stock, quite a long, deep bag, which I fitted with a strong manilla string to pass over my shoulder and hang by my side.

My next task was to get together plenty of wood for my precious fire during the night. But this was an easy affair, the very edge of the grove abounding in fallen and dried branches of every kind and description.

I made another trip to the gulls' eggs, equipped in my new hat and with my bag slung at my side, and returned with it filled with as many as I desired, and for contingencies I boiled quite a large number of them in salt water in my meat-can over the fire.

As a last thing, I went to the field and brought back an armful of grass, which I strewed under my cedar-tree, and increased it with a large bundle of dried seaweed for bed-clothing, and a good-sized stone for a pillow. Having completed all these arrangements, eaten again of my gulls' eggs and baked clams, and carefully attended to my fire, I cut up some of the small quantity of tobacco remaining to me with my clam-shell, and placing it in my pipe had a quiet smoke.

By this time the sun was sinking to rest, and I took care to make the record of the day upon the boat-planking, and also opened a calendar account upon one of the branches of my cedar-tree by means of my pointed nail and clam-shell.

As the dusk came on I began to think, What is the next most important thing for me to do? My mind answered me, Preserve your fire, or invent means so that you can light it without trouble. I should say that I had already burned a piece of the cotton lining of my trousers, and carefully preserved it between two clean, large sea-clam shells for tinder.

I thought that I saw my way clear to protect my fire on the morrow, and also to give myself some weapons of offence, and after having asked God's pity upon my condition I dropped asleep in my seaweed bed, thinking of these things, with my fire near by me well covered up with ashes.

CHAPTER VI.

Build fireplace. Make knife and spear from anchor. Build tower of stones for perpetual lamps. Resolve to explore the island.

I SLEPT soundly and pleasantly all night, and jumped out of bed in the early morning light, ran to the beach, and had a nice plunge in the smooth and sparkling waters. Just as I was about to leave the water I espied two or three quite large dog-fish sharks, which were four or five feet in length, and, although I had no fears of them as concerned myself, they immediately gave me an idea of how I could utilize them could I succeed in capturing them. I ran back to the bank, got into my clothes, and, you may be well sure, knew that the fire was all right even before I started to bathe; ran again to the seaside and dug a few clams, and filled the bailer with salt water, and soon had my usual meal of boiled eggs and roast clams under way. Whilst my breakfast was cooking I commenced building, and completed a superior kind of fireplace, with nice, strong sides of stone, set up on edge, and just wide enough apart to sustain my condenser. After having eaten my breakfast, quenched my thirst, and had a good, quiet smoke, I set the fresh-water apparatus to work again, and commenced to apply myself to the task of the day. With my clam-shell I cut the manilla warp from the anchor, and the latter lay before me under my fixed gaze. I saw that the stock, which was of iron also, was passed through a hole in the solid iron forming the shank of the anchor, and was retained by a shoulder on one side and a large ball at the extremity of its arm on the other. My first attempt was to unship this iron stock or arm from the rest of the anchor, and release it from the hole through which it was rove and kept in place. To effect this I set up in the sand a large stone, with quite a flat, smooth top, as my anvil, and procured another, of an oblong, irregular shape, which I could grasp with my right hand, and with which I could strike quite a powerful blow, as my hammer. Thus equipped, I started a nice fire in my new fireplace and put the condenser on that, leaving me the open fire for my blacksmith's shop. I next went to the beach and got a piece of kelp, and with my clam-shell cut it into suitable lengths for my purpose, and, thrusting the ball at the end of the anchor-stock into the fire, I commenced operations.

To increase the heat of the fire I piled on the sort of semi-charcoal that had been formed by the wood covered in the ashes the night before, and sprinkled the same carefully with a little water, and to still further promote affairs I thrust one end of my pieces of kelp under the warm ashes, towards the bottom and centre of the fire, and by putting the other end to my lips I forced a blast of air through the flames as nicely as if I had had a pair of bellows. The iron soon became red-hot, and, snatching it out of the fire and on to my anvil, I, by a few well-directed blows, soon had the ball reduced so as to be able to unship the stock from the rest of the anchor, and held in my hand a bar of iron about an inch in diameter and three feet long; quite a weapon in itself, but not sufficient for such a mechanic as I was.

I took this bar of iron, and, putting the end again in the fire, commenced upon my kelp bellows, and soon pulled it out, quite hot and malleable. Suffice it to say that in not a very long space of time, and by repeated beatings and hammerings, I had fashioned out quite a respectable knife, of about eight inches in length and at least quarter of an inch thick in the back; and although the sides were a little wavy and irregular, I knew that grinding would nearly take that out. Whilst the knife that I had made was still fastened to the original bar of iron I drew it down to a long, thin point, and by grasping it and bending it to the right and left soon had it free.

My next task was to temper this piece of metal, and by repeatedly plunging it into water and back into the fire I soon got it quite hard, and fit for my present purposes. I sought out a coarse-grained stone, and with my tin of water sat down to moisten it and grind my knife to an edge. I passed several hours at this work, but in the end found myself possessed of quite a good-looking knife, with a good sharp point and fair edge. I picked up a suitable piece of wood for a handle, and soon had it in shape, and, slightly heating the pointed, unfinished end, I drove it home with a stone firmly into the handle, and my knife was done. Pleased enough was I with my success; but I did not stop here. The hole in the shank of the anchor, whence I had drawn the stock, fascinated me. I saw before me a hammer of iron, all ready made to my hand. I thrust the anchor into the fire just below this hole, towards the flukes, and set my kelp bellows to work with a will. After repeated heatings and poundings I had brought the iron down to so small a size that I was able, as before, to part it from the original bar, by bending it backward and forward till the crystallization of the iron was destroyed, exactly as you break off a nail by hitting it with a hammer a few times in opposite directions. I had to get the ring off at the end of the anchor in the same manner, and then found myself in possession of a piece of iron almost exactly like what we sailors call a top-maul, a flat-headed hammer with a long end. I speedily fitted this with a good, strong handle, and, after beating it and tempering it to the best of my ability, put it into use at once. Taking the bar from which I had made my knife I soon made it take the shape of a kind of spear, or rather harpoon, with a sharp, flat head, similar to those arrows always printed on charts to show the direction of currents or winds.

This, when finished, tempered, ground, and lashed firmly to a smooth staff of wood, some two inches in diameter and eight feet in length, was really a formidable weapon, either for offence or defence.

Armed with my harpoon and knife, I made my way to the seaside, having still another project in my head. Proud, indeed, was I of my weapons, and my natural courage was increased. I took off my clothes and waded quietly into the water, and had not long to wait till I saw some of my friends the dog-sharks, and picking out one that suited me,—for I had no difficulty in approaching them, they showing no fear of me,—I thrust my harpoon into him, and dragged him ashore, cut him open with my knife, took out his liver, and dragged back the carcase into the sea. I served three of them in this manner. From the last one—which was the largest and had a beautiful skin—I cut a large strip, out of which to make a case for my knife, which I did whilst it was green, fitting it nicely, and also a small tip to cover the barbs of my harpoon when not in use. I sewed these up, or, rather, fastened them by means of a bradawl sharpened in the fire from one of the boat nails, tempered and fitted with a handle, and nice, strong thread made from my manilla rope. I brought back with me to the fireplace quite a good-sized flounder, that I had also speared without the slightest trouble, and it was soon cut up and broiling away for my dinner, it being now about noon. I hung my shark livers in the sun, upon a tree, a little distant from my camp, where they would not offend me, and placed myself at table, the fish being now cooked, and plenty of cold boiled eggs on hand.

I could spare no time for much dinner. My condenser had been taken off long ago in the forenoon, my two meat-cans being full of water. After dinner I stopped to take a few whiffs at my pipe, and then to work again, for I had much to do ere the setting of the sun. In the first place I proceeded to the right of my camp a short distance, and had no difficulty in picking up as many large shells as I desired, some of them being fully a foot in circumference, and beautiful enough, with their pink, open mouths, to ornament the table of any lady. I gathered together some fifteen or twenty of these, and transported them to the seaside, and thence to my camp, having washed them out carefully, and ascertaining that they would each hold about a quart or more of water. I then set my condenser hard at work, determined to get a supply ahead of any contingency.

For my next task I got hold of the breaker that contained my books and charts, and by means of my hammer soon had the hoops off and the head out. But I was mortified to see that a little water had worked into the cask, and that the motion of the boat had caused the books, in moving to and fro, to completely destroy the chart, and, with the little water that had entered, reduced it to a pulp and beyond recognition and repair. Tears started into my eyes at this cruel blow of fate, and it was with the greatest anxiety that I seized upon the books and examined them. Their strong canvas covers had preserved them, and although battered, chafed, and damp they seemed intact,—all except the Nautical Almanac, which had suffered somewhat in different portions, to what extent I had now no time to examine minutely. My Compendium of Useful Arts and Sciences, and Bowditch's Navigator, were, at least, saved, and these were a library and tower of strength in themselves. I put the three books carefully in the sun, where they might dry, and, after heading up the breaker again and setting on the hoops strongly and firmly, I went back to where I had gathered my shells and fastened on to one that I had before discovered, that would hold many gallons,—it is called, I think, sometimes, a sea oyster. With this burden I struggled along to my tree where I had hung the sharks' livers, and placed this huge basin under them to catch the dripping oil; and, as I did not expect much result for a day or two, I cut off a portion of one of the livers and took it to my fireside and carefully tried it out in small pieces, in numerous clam-shells, and poured the oil thus obtained into one of my shell reservoirs.

My next task was to go back into my grass-field and gather some of the clayey earth that I had noticed there, and to bring it in my hat to the camp, getting a sufficient quantity in two trips. With this clayey earth I mixed pounded-up clam-shells and a small quantity of seaweed, fine sand, and water. Then, near my cedar-tree, and protected by it, I built a tower of flat stones, using this material as mortar. I built it in a circular form, of about two feet in diameter, and perhaps three feet high. At the bottom I left interstices every once in a while, varying in size, but none of them larger than a half inch in diameter. Towards the top I left the same kind of airholes, but rather larger in size. On one side, about half way up, I left two stones so that they could be taken out by hand and replaced, and when taken out would leave quite a large aperture, large enough to put my arm into and explore the interior. In the exact centre of this stone circular tower I drove a strong stake, standing at least three feet higher than the walls, and by means of sedge, rushes, manilla twine, and large leaves I made the pointed top—of which this stake was the apex, and the top of the circular wall the base—completely waterproof, the sedge projecting beyond the walls in every direction.

Within this tower I placed my flint-stone, steel, and tinder, and upon four smooth stones that I placed inside I fitted up on each a large sea-clam shell full of shark's-liver oil, and from milkweed pods provided each of them with a soft, cottony wick, which I lighted, and then closed the aperture. By peeping through the interstices I could see that my lamps burned splendidly, and by blowing I was unable to get up any current inside. My gigantic lantern was made. If my fire should go out, my flint and steel fail me, here was perpetual light. I placed four lights within, so that in case the roof should leak a drop in a heavy rain, some one or two of the shells would run a chance of not being put out. I did not intend to allow my fire to go out this night, but to burn the lamps as a test only of how much oil they would need, and how they would appear in the morning, so as to know what to expect should I leave them for any length of time.

Fixing my lamp-tower and pouring the condensed water into the breaker, getting wood for the fire, and my other labors, had made the day a hard one; but as the sun went down, and I supped upon the remains of my fish warmed up, and the inevitable eggs, and enjoyed my pipe, I could but think of how far I had advanced even in one twenty-four hours. Weapons by my side, a breaker full of fresh water, and perpetual light in a waterproof tower beside me. With the deepening shadows came, however, the bitter feelings of desolation and solitude, mingled with the uncertainty of the magnitude of my island, and the impossibility of my being able, except by exploration, to prove it uninhabited.

During this day my heart jumped into my mouth many times when I heard the least unusual noise, or, carelessly glancing up, mistook every tree for a savage. My complete freedom from any annoyance up to the present time was in itself satisfactory to my mind, and strong probable reason that the island was unpeopled. Then its unknown position—for I felt convinced that there was no known land where I was now sitting—improved the probabilities. I foresaw that my next task would be the exploration of the island and a search for fresh water; and, wondering what the future would bring forth, I rolled drowsily over into my seaweed bed, and dropped asleep in the very act.

CHAPTER VII.

Improve my lamp-tower. Make a bow and arrow, and fish-hooks and lines. Capture a large turtle. Improve my steel and flint, and build a hut. Procure some salt, and make arrangements to explore the island on the morrow.

I AROSE at sunrise and found another lovely day commencing. God had blessed me with pleasant weather each day so far. I went first to my calendar, and with the point of my knife inscribed the day and date, as usual; thence to my lamp-tower, and found all the lamps burning splendidly, but with not oil enough to have lasted more than two or three hours more. I foresaw that I must get a much larger and more shallow dish to have any certainty of keeping them alight for any length of time without replenishing them each morning and night. The principle upon which they were built was exactly that which I had often observed in the northern part of China, where the Chinese burn peanut oil in exactly the same way in shallow dishes, with a pith wick hanging over the side. The principle involved necessitated a shallow dish, and that the wick should be in nearly a horizontal position, to suck up the oil to its end which projected over the side of the clam-shell. If the reservoir for the oil was deep instead of shallow, the receding of the oil as it was consumed by the wick would soon let the lamp go out. I saw that I should have to improve upon my lamp business, and concluded to work out the problem whilst taking my morning bath and breakfast. As I started towards the beach, I saw at a little distance to my left a huge turtle, the first I had seen, making for the sea. I ran with my utmost speed, and contrived to upset him upon his back before he had reached it, and soon dragged him to my fireplace, and, although still upon his back, for fear of any accident or escape, at once beheaded him then and there. I then quietly took off my clothes and had my usual bath, taking care, however, not to go out of my depth, as I saw several dog-fish sharks, and possibly larger ones of their species might be in the bay, but, from its shallowness, I did not much think it. Whilst bathing, I solved my problem about the lamps, and returned in good spirits to my fire and clothes, and soon had a nice turtle soup boiling and a steak of the same broiling upon the embers.

This turtle was a godsend, and was just what I needed to change my diet. I made a hearty meal, and with reluctance cut into the small piece of tobacco left me and filled my pipe, and had a short smoke, and then to work. I took two of my largest conch-shells, that would hold nearly a quart a-piece, and filled the lips up with my mortar that I had used the day before in the construction of the lamp-tower, leaving an orifice at the larger end, of sufficient size to pour liquid into easily, and one at the smaller end very small indeed. I then thrust both of the shells into the hot embers, and hardened the mortar or cement so that it was soon dry and compact. I then went to my grass-field and chose some minute grass-straws of about a foot in length, and inserted two in the small orifice of each shell, and fixed them in with moist cement. I then went to my lamp-tower, took the roof carefully off, and with a base of stones, and by means of twine with which I fastened them to the central stake, soon had my shells lashed and secured in an upright position, with the four straws pointing into the four clam-shell lamps. I then went with my bailer to the large sea-oyster shell and dipped up the oil that had distilled under the rays of the sun from the dog-sharks' livers, and in several trips filled my shell-reservoirs with oil, and had the satisfaction of seeing each straw dropping oil into the clam-shell lamp beneath. The dropping being rather fast, I easily regulated it by thrusting seaweed stoppers into the upper orifice of the shells till the feeding was very slow, but very perfect and exact. I felt now that I could leave my tower, days without care, and be sure of finding the lamps burning upon my return. I carefully replaced the roof, lighted the lamps again, and made all snug and secure. I did all this work about the lamps to make myself doubly sure of always having fire. I was well aware that with my hardened knife I could strike fire much better than I at first did with my shoe-nail, but I wanted to be sure and take every precaution, and to that end I went to work upon the nails in the boat-planking, and, finding one to my mind, I flattened it out at my anvil into a narrow ribbon of iron, which I hardened and steeled in the fire and water; and, after carefully testing it with my flint, which, by the way, I broke into several fragments, I put it and a piece of the flint into my pocket, and returned the remaining fragments with another nail, hardened and heated in the same manner, to the custody of the lamp-tower. I took thence a small quantity of the burned tinder I had made of my clothing, some of the nigger-ball powder, and cotton of the milkweed, and taking one of the numerous pods of last year's growth that I had gathered of these, and also stored there out of the rain, I split it lengthwise with my knife, and removed most of the core and cotton, and in its place inserted the tinder and powder that I have just mentioned, and secured the whole together by winding round about it some manilla twine; and, not satisfied with that, I cut a small piece from my flannel shirt and wrapped that also about it, and secured it with twine. Thus I carried on my person the means of starting a fire at any time; and, feeling secure, I allowed myself to throw this terrible fear off my mind.

CAPTURING A TURTLE.—Page 66.

All my energies were pointing to one direction,—to be able to arm and equip myself, so as to make the tour of my island as speedily as possible; but I foresaw that, with my utmost speed and care, I should not be able to be ready to start until the morrow, if then. I went into my grass-field and passed beyond it into the natural undergrowth of trees, and soon had picked out exactly what I wanted, a sort of ash or walnut tree, evidently dead some time since from some cause, the limbs of which I tested and found of the right elasticity. I cut off with my knife several portions that suited my purpose, and returning to my fire, I soon had a handsome bow of fine elasticity, some six feet in length, finished to my hand. From a lighter kind of wood, a sort of alder, I manufactured without much difficulty some half-dozen arrows, and sharpened and hardened as many nails to form heads for them, which I securely lashed on with fine manilla twine. I then proceeded to my gulls' nests retreat, and picked up such feathers as I thought might suit me, and also brought back a load of fresh eggs in my bag.

I then took off my clothes again and waded into the sea with my harpoon, and soon had on shore one of my dog-shark friends, and his bladder and fins in a short time in my bailer over a slow fire, for I wanted some glue badly. I took occasion, whilst this was preparing, to thoroughly oil my bow and arrows and to wipe them off nice and clean again with leaves and seaweed.

I soon had plenty of glue, and of a good quality also, which I poured out into a large clam-shell, and filled my bailer again with water to boil and cleanse it out. I then proceeded with great care to lay up three strands of fine manilla, about ten feet long each, and made each of them fast to a tree near each other; and, stretched as, they were in this manner, I saturated them with the liquid glue, and then brought them together and laid them up right-handed, so as to make a very fine-looking and strong bowstring, with which I was delighted. By means of the glue I easily fitted each arrow with three nice feathers, and I also dipped the seizing round the heads, that held on the iron barbs, into the same, which gave them a fine finish and smoothed down all the standing fibres of the manilla twine, making all "ship-shape and Bristol fashion," as sailors say.

Whilst my hand was in I made also a fishing-line of great strength and of considerable length, and managed to forge out two quite respectable fish-hooks from the wrought nails of the boat's planking. I took my usual meal at noon, but it was of delicious turtle soup, instead of fish, clams, or eggs, none of which did I, however, by any means despise. After dinner I sat down and sharpened and perfected the points of my arrow-heads and fish-hooks. I was not able to make any barbs to the latter, but had to run the risk, when I hooked a fish, never to let him have any slack line till he was landed.

Having finished these various labors and looked after my condenser, I commenced another round tower similar to the one already built, and near to it. I wanted a place of safety for books, and with the stones at hand and some new mixed mortar, or cement, I in a few hours completed my task, and had the pleasure of seeing them in safety from rain or damp. I was afraid to put them in the lamp-tower for fear of their catching fire in some unforeseen manner, and I would not risk the chance, however remote it might be.

This being finished, I went to the wood and cut down with my knife several small trees, about six feet in height, leaving a crotch like the letter Y at the top of each. I brought these near my cedar-tree, and with my hammer drove them into the ground, so that they stood at an equal height of about four feet in the front row and one foot in the rear row. I stopped this work for a season to fill the bailer, which I had cleansed of the glue, with salt water, and let it, during the afternoon, gradually boil down several times, till I had collected quite a quantity of salt. After attending to this, I returned to my hut-building, and soon had the uprights crossed with light sticks and branches, and upon these I placed large masses of sedge as thatch, which I kept in place by numerous flat stones that I placed upon the roof. I wove into both the long sides, and one end, some manilla strands and pliable small branches, working them in and out in a horizontal position and at right angles to the uprights. To this rough basket work, or trellis, I bound, by means of more manilla strands, large bundles of sedge, till I had a nice hut of about eight feet in length and six wide, with one end left open some two feet wide, and the roof four feet high on one side fronting the sea and two feet high on the land side. Into this hut I carried all my few earthly treasures, and made me a nice bed of seaweed and sedge on one side, and with a large clam-shell and the flukes of the anchor cut out a nice trench round about it, under the overhanging eaves, and piled the spare earth up against the sides of the hut. I was proud of my work. After everything was all finished to my satisfaction, I sat down to a hearty meal, and, being too tired even to smoke, I pulled a small cedar-tree that I had cut down for the purpose, against the opening in the end of my hut, from the inside, and threw myself upon my seaweed bed, and fell instantly to sleep.

CHAPTER VIII.

Rainy day. Reflections concerning climate, season of the year, tides, etc. Plant several varieties of my seeds. Make a pocket compass, and prepare for my exploration of the island.

"MAN proposes, but God disposes." This was what I thought when I woke in the morning and looked out upon a foggy, drizzling day; not very much wind, but a regular Scotch mist, and with every look of settling into a real downright rain. I could not well complain, for I had been blessed with pleasant weather since my arrival, and it was but natural that all days should not be as pleasant; and the fast-approaching appearance of rain delighted me in another sense, for I was not at all sure about my supply of fresh water, and I was not sorry to see that the island was visited with rain, which I foresaw that in the future I could utilize should all other methods fail. My nautical experience had been correct; in less than an hour the rain fell freely, and the wind got up quite strong from the northward and eastward. I saw that I must put aside all idea of exploring my island for this day, and I was not sorry, as I had several things that I desired to complete first, and my great fear of not being able to obtain plenty of water of a good quality was fast being dissipated. I got to my fire and started it briskly, so that it would not be disturbed by the rain, and for more security lighted a small one inside my hut under cover, so as to run no risks at all. Although I felt confident that I had the means at present of starting a new fire at any time, I was morbid on this subject, and could not prevail upon myself to allow any of the three flames to be extinguished, namely, the lamps, the regular fire, and the small one in my hut, so fearful was I about it. Up to the present time fire was not only fire to me, but it was water. Once secure concerning the latter I felt that I could allow my fires to go out with better faith. I found during this day my hut a great comfort, and blessed my stars that I had completed it so luckily before this storm commenced. The rain was not cold, being from the direction of the equator; and I therefore, throughout the day, moved about in it in my flannel shirt and drawers, with my broad-brimmed hat and shoes and stockings, leaving my other clothing dry in the hut. I was pleased to observe that the thatching was a perfect success, and the interior as dry and nice as possible. My first task was to go and get the other half of the sea-oyster shell that I had placed under my shark's livers and bring it near the house. I had no fears of the rain interfering with the former, for I knew that, although exposed, the rain would not mix with the oil, but would, if anything, purify it, and that I could easily skim off every particle with a clam-shell when the weather became again clear. Having got my sea-oyster shell, which would hold some gallons, placed under one of the dripping eaves of my hut, I sat down to breakfast, which I made very pleasantly of turtle steaks and eggs. After breakfast I drew forth from my trousers pocket my precious piece of tobacco, and looked with grief at its diminished proportions, but, urged on by solitude and the rain, I could not resist filling my pipe and taking a good long smoke. Whilst smoking, the following thoughts of what I had seen, and what I might expect ran through my head, and I repeated them to myself to fix them in my memory, so that they might serve me in the future. In the first place I calculated that this day, the thirteenth of November, must in this part of the world represent the thirteenth of May in the northern hemisphere, and that therefore I was in the very spring-time of the year, and at a proper season to plant some of my seeds and note the result. Although I did not know how far south I was, still I knew within a degree or so by the reckoning that I had on board of the "Good Luck." I felt assured that I was somewhere between the fortieth and forty-fifth parallel of latitude, and that the climate must therefore be somewhat like that of countries situated between the same parallels of north latitude, like that of England, France, or the New England States of America. Knowing this I had a sort of general knowledge of what seeds would probably prosper, and also what kind of a winter I might expect. Surrounded as I was, as I suspected, by water, I thought that the winter ought to be milder than those of the northern hemisphere, and for the same reason the summers milder. I remembered that many fruits would mature in England, in latitude 52° north, that would not grow in the open air in New England in only 42° north. In imagination I gave my island a climate even milder than England, first on account of its being nearer the equator, and next on account of its, as I supposed, small extent, completely surrounded by water. I was also led to this belief by the balmy, spring-like, and warm air of the days I had already passed upon the island, and the advancement in vegetation that I saw upon all sides of me; the latter completely satisfying me that the springs must be very early, and that the winters could not be very severe. I had also noticed that the rise and fall of the tide was considerable; I should say at a venture at least ten feet. I had no doubt but what I could wade almost across the gulf separating me from the breakwater at mean low tide, at any rate a few strokes only of swimming would be necessary, I felt convinced. From these subjects I passed to thinking of my lonely fate, and made up my mind to cross over again to the breakwater this very day and examine anew the scene of my disaster. What a miserable fate was reserved for me. Here was I only thirty-two years of age, in the very prime of my life, cut off from intercourse with all my fellow-men; cast upon a desert island, without even the comforts and necessities that my predecessor in history had given him to his hands, with nothing but the few miserable trifles that I have enumerated;

cast on shore, to care for myself, protect myself, and live for whatever God might have in store for me. The bitter tears ran through my fingers at the desolate picture my imagination had conjured up. Why was I punished in this manner? what had I done that I should be imprisoned in this solitude? But then, on the other hand, what should prevent me from building in the future a boat or raft and escaping from my prison, or why should I despair of some day seeing a vessel within sight of my island that I could hail?

My greatest fear, I found in consultation with myself, was the fear of savages; that the island was inhabited. This made me shudder with fright; I felt that I should never rest easy till I had explored it from end to end; I felt that I must do this, and at the very earliest moment. I knew, too, that I ought each day to have crossed to the breakwater and to have looked for some passing ship, but my fire and water and weapons had taken all my time and attention. I made up my mind to attend to this better in future, but then again my sailor's knowledge gave me little to hope for from this source; nothing but the accident of the ocean, or exploration, or discovery, would, I felt confident, ever bring a vessel in this direction. This gave me the horrors again, for my mind convinced me that I might live my lifetime on this island without any reasonable hope of ever seeing a vessel approach it. The very fact of its not being laid down on any chart in so late a year as 1865 proved to me conclusively two facts,—one that it must be quite small in extent, and the other that it was wholly and completely, as I felt that it was, out of the course of vessels engaged in any pursuit, and the chances of its discovery exceedingly small.

My meditations were abruptly ended by the hissing of the ashes in the heel of my pipe, and I sadly arose and placed it carefully away, and betook myself to my labors for the day. I knew that it must be at this time about low water, and as the clothing I had on was already quite wet, I started forth, without undressing, to the beach, and, armed with my harpoon, waded in and headed for the breakwater. I found, as I supposed, that with the exception of about fifteen or twenty yards in the middle, which I was compelled to swim, I could wade the whole distance. I soon arrived at the opposite side and clambered up the rocks. I could see but little way seaward on account of the rain and slight fog, but at my feet was the same uneasy, treacherous sea, that had swallowed up my shipmates. I could find no sign of the boat or of them, and I knew that whatever articles lay at the base of these rocks would by this time either be buried deep from human eye or destroyed by the everlasting motion of the undertow. The bottom also, to judge by the sides of the rocks, was no doubt covered with kelp and rock-weed, amongst which, even on land, it would be almost impossible to find anything; how much more so at the bottom of the ocean! I gave up all thought of ever recovering anything more from the boat, and sadly and silently retook my way back to my hut. This trip, and looking after my fresh water and lamps and fire and wood, took up my forenoon and brought me to dinner, which, although lonely, I enjoyed. I took this opportunity to also cook some spare pieces of the turtle and to gather them together in layers, with salt between, to serve me for food in my proposed exploration. I cooked and prepared quite a quantity, as I did also of the boiled eggs. After dinner and the cooking and preparing of these rations, I started forth upon a more important business. I went to my field in the rear of the hut, and picking out one corner where the soil seemed fair, I, by the aid of the fluke of my anchor, turned up the soil in some twenty-five or thirty places, in a circular form, some twenty-four inches in diameter, and carefully removed the turf. I knew that with my tools I could not expect to plough or spade up any portion of great extent, so I took this means. I left the sward intact, except in these circular places, some six or eight feet apart, which I prepared for my seeds, and sparingly from each I planted the following: in five of them, apple seeds; in another five of them, pear seeds; in another five, grape seeds; and in the same and other ones, cucumbers, beans, squashes, celery, blackberries, strawberries, tomatoes, lettuce, etc. My wheat, rye, and rice, I carefully kept on hand, with the exception of one plat that I sowed with wheat wholly, simply as a precaution to preserve the seed if it should mature. Having finished this labor, I commenced upon another task, one that was to tax my ingenuity, namely, a compass. I did not feel like undertaking the examination of the island without this useful instrument. I first procured some nice, strong, birch-bark, sound and well seasoned, of which there was plenty in the grove, and by means of my sharpened nail awl and manilla thread soon had formed a nice little box of about three inches in diameter and two high, with a good-fitting cover to same. By means of a piece of manilla thread held firmly by my thumb on a nice, flat piece of bark, and the awl fastened to the other extremity, I had no difficulty in marking out a disc that would fit within the circumference of my box. I soon cut this out with my knife, and by means of a straight stick and a small piece of charcoal and some little measurement, soon had it marked off into thirty-two points; making the north point with an arrow-head to distinguish it, and the other cardinal points large and black. I soon had quite a respectable compass-card before me. I then took one of the wrought nails from the boat-planking, and, in spite of the rain, soon had it beaten out on my anvil into a narrow ribbon, which I hardened and converted into steel of the length of the diameter of my compass-card or disc. By repeated poundings and drawing this ribbon over my knife from heel to point, I magnetized it so that it would adhere to iron or steel quite forcibly. I fastened this upon the underside of my compass-cover with fine manilla thread near each extremity. I should have said that whilst this ribbon was red hot, I had forced, with another nail, quite a large hole, perhaps three-eighths of an inch in diameter, through its centre. I broke out one of the teeth of my horn hair-comb and lashed it firmly for an upright into the centre of my box, and over the centre of my compass-card I cut out a hole of about an inch in diameter, and over this fastened a little cone about the size of a woman's thimble, only coming to a peak, instead of a round head, and about an inch in height, also made of bark. Into this cone I forced a small piece of the polished lip of one of my sea shells, as an agate or face upon which my horn pivot was to rest and the disc rotate. Passing the disc into the box and the horn pivot up through the hole in the magnet into the inverted cup or cone containing the small portion of shell, I found that I had a real, quick, and good compass. The card had to be balanced by placing, with my glue, small portions of bark on its underneath surface till it floated evenly upon its pivot, and my task was done. I felt that with this implement I could not get lost in my explorations, and although rude in construction, its value was as sterling as one made of brass and with paper disc. I filled the whole box with the soft cotton of my milkweed pods, both above and below the card, and put on the cover so that there could be no motion to wear the pivot. I only, of course, intended to use it in case of necessity, and I had then only to carefully open it, remove the card and cotton, and set it back upon its pivot, after placing it carefully on the ground and protecting it from any sudden blast of wind. I was proud of my instrument, and felt much more secure, in its possession, as to my ability to explore the island successfully.

This ended my day's work, and the setting sun gave signs of a pleasant day for the morrow. I felt pleased that I had planted my seeds during the rain, which would give them a good start, and sat down to my supper with a feeling that I had again overcome some of the difficulties that surrounded me. I visited my oyster-shell outside the eaves, and although the sky had been for an hour or two fast clearing up, I saw that I had several gallons of pure rain water, for which I was, I hope, duly thankful. I meditated upon the morrow. Upon my exploration depended all my security for the future. Should I find the island inhabited, a long farewell to all content. If uninhabited, I could, I felt certain, take care of myself till it pleased God to remove me from the solitude to which I was tied. I envied the old Robinson Crusoe, to whom I likened myself, and thought, why could not I have been as fortunate as he; if the "Good Luck" must be destroyed why could she not have come ashore on this island where I could have saved something from her, and, more precious yet, some of the lives of my shipmates? How many years must I stagnate on this island? But I am young and determined to improve my position. Have I not a book of all the practical sciences to aid me in forcing Nature to give up her secrets? Why should I not be able to improve my condition far beyond that which my predecessor in history had been able to do? He had not the education of the nineteenth century to aid him; he knew nothing about the science of steam, railroads, steamboats, telegraphs, etc, whilst I had a book treating of these and a thousand other subjects of infinite interest. I could not help thinking that if I could find iron, I could do almost anything, and why should I not be able to find it? I knew that it was a metal like gold, disseminated throughout all parts of the earth. By my labors as a boy in it I felt that I could, as a mechanic, do almost anything if I could discover this ore, and coal to smelt it. If I found water, I felt assured of the future, and I could not but believe that my exploration would enable me to discover that. It was impossible that so large an area as my eye could gather in should be without it. Once found, I felt no fears for food. I felt assured of my physical well-being, and the climate, I felt convinced, could not be very severe in the winter months with such delightful weather in this spring month of November. I could in time build some kind of a boat, and reach the Society Islands to the northward of me, or the South American coast to the eastward, or even New Zealand to the westward. I was not without hope, and, although far from cheerful in my dreadful solitude, I could not but think that I should be comparatively happy and contented if I felt sure of my island being uninhabited; but I dreaded, in my exploration about to be undertaken, to come suddenly upon some savage village, that would destroy all my desire to still live, and almost put me in a mood to take my own life with my own hands.

My nerves were unstrung now all the time, and the slightest noise caused my heart to palpitate with fear, as it had never before done in the severest gale at sea or in face of the greatest practical dangers. I was fast becoming a coward, and felt that I should continue to be one till my problem was solved; then, if successful in ascertaining the extent of the island and its freedom from savages, I felt that I could resign myself with fortitude to the designs that Providence had in my behalf. These thoughts brought me well into the evening, and, commending myself to the divine care, I lay down upon my sea-weed couch and dropped to sleep.

CHAPTER IX.

Exploration of the island: First day. Fresh water at Rapid River. Wild goats, quail, tortoise, tobacco, wild ducks, trout, sweet potatoes, mussels. Name the island and principal points, etc.

I AROSE very early in the morning and saw that I was to be favored with a very pleasant day. I went to the seaside and took my usual bath; thence to my lamp-tower and arranged all the wicks and reservoirs for a long burning; then to breakfast, which I quickly dispatched, and then my preparation to start, which consisted of the following: I first filled my powder canister with nice, pure rain-water, and fitted it with sennit straps of manilla to hang on my back, taking care to put the screw in the head solidly home, so that it would not leak. In my bag made of sedges I stowed my boiled eggs and turtle-steaks, already cooked, also several other articles of value rolled up in different parcels of birch-bark, including my fishing-line and hooks, and some spare manilla strands, and bradawl, and carefully wrapped up my compass and several large pieces of birch-bark and charcoal, intending to make a sketch of the island as I explored it, being in my younger days quite a good draughtsman. In my trousers pocket I placed my pipe and tobacco, my flint and steel, and my tinder, tied up in my milkweed pod. I then slung over my back my bow and arrows, the latter in a light quiver of birch-bark that I had made for them; secured my knife in its shark-skin sheath about my waist, and took my harpoon in my hand, and, thus accoutred, started forth.

Before I advanced in any direction I bethought myself that I would commence by naming the island and all prominent parts that my eye could take in, and to continue this during my exploration. Accordingly I walked down and faced the breakwater, and, drawing forth a piece of birch-bark and charcoal, sketched rudely the outline before me. Determined as I was to succeed, and remembering that I had overcome the want of water and fire, I deliberately named the island *Perseverance Island.* The point that ended the breakwater slightly to the westward of me I named *Point Deliverance*; the reef in front of me, the *Breakwater*, the water between me and the Breakwater, *Stillwater Cove*, on account of its uniform quietness, being almost land-locked.

Having finished this I gave one long look of affection upon my miserable hut, and, with a mental prayer for aid and assistance, struck out on the pure, white, sandy beach towards the eastward part of the island. I went naturally in this direction first, for I was too good a sailor to walk around the island left-handed, or, as we say at sea, "against the sun." I had just enough superstition to believe that such a course would have brought me bad luck. I followed my beach about one mile and a half, having on my left hand Stillwater Cove, and on my right hand small groves of tree with long vistas between them, giving me a view into the interior of the island, and over fields of natural grass. I often left the beach to inspect these openings, which I approached with perfect awe, expecting every moment to chance upon some native village, or other sign of the presence of man. But nothing of the kind occurred. And yet before I reached the end of my beach I met with so startling an adventure that I was unmanned for over an hour, and had to sit down and rest before proceeding on my journey. Approaching one of these openings or glades I peered in as usual, keeping myself on my hands and knees, to see if I could find any signs of my dreaded enemies. But the place was as peaceful as any of the others, and, standing up to my full height, I gave vent to a sigh of relief, when, without a moment's notice or warning, some three or four forms jumped from the long grass where they had been concealed and made for the thickets further inland. I was so frightened that I sank to the earth nearly senseless. But as my mind was just about to leave me I had force of character enough to observe that they were not savages, but animals. The revulsion, however, was too great, and I sat down in a faint and sick state, as I have related. When I could collect my mind I easily recognized the shapes I had seen as some species of goats, and delighted indeed was I at the discovery. But it immediately set me thinking, How could there be goats on this island? I well knew that they would not be here naturally; that they must have been put here, and probably by some whaler, for those vessels I well knew often carry several of these animals with them. But if they had been placed upon the island thus, why was it not reported, why was it not known? I could conceive of only one reason, and that was that the unfortunate vessel that had discovered it had afterwards been lost, and therefore its existence had again become unknown. But this was only theory on my part. The quickness with which they left me showed that they were wild, and probably had been many years upon the island. If I should see only this flock of four or five I should feel as if some of the human race had, within a comparatively short time, visited the island. But if in my explorations I should fall upon more of these creatures, I should know that they had propagated and increased through untold years, and from a commencement that would never be revealed.

Having completely overcome my faintness, and rejoiced at my discovery, I passed back to the beach, and in a few moments came to a place where it turned abruptly to the right. The land also, being quite rocky and of some elevation, obstructed my view, and, preparing my bow and arrow in one hand and my harpoon in the other, I crept round the bend cautiously on my hands and knees. A beautiful sight struck my eyes. To my right hand, and within a hundred yards of me, a dashing, sparkling waterfall of some eight or ten feet in height, and fifteen or twenty wide, poured its waters into Stillwater Cove; and beyond and inland as far as my eye could reach, till the river mixed with the foliage on either bank, and was undistinguishable, I saw smaller and less abrupt falls of water coming down the gorge between the hillsides; in short, a large mountain brook or small river, bubbling and gurgling its way to dash itself at last over a fall into Stillwater Cove.

I forgot all about savages and natives, and, dashing down my weapons, I rushed towards the fall, where it fell into the cove, and, holding my hands under it, filled them with what my mouth proved to me to be soft, pure, fresh river water. I danced, I sung; I was for a little time as crazy as a loon, and here had I been distilling water and racking my brains for days to provide, and a bubbling, running brook, almost a river, within at least two miles of me all the time. But in my happiness I soon forgot my past labors and distress, all that was gone by. Here was a supply of water that kind Heaven had granted me, inexhaustible, and of delicious coolness and taste. Having returned a little to my senses, I went back for my weapons, and sat down and enjoyed the scene before me. It was indeed beautiful. I saw that I was at the head of Stillwater Cove, and that by crossing upon the stones below the fall I should be on the side of the Breakwater, which I now saw was part of the mainland, being a narrow peninsula running nearly east and west, and enclosing Stillwater Cove, and joining the mainland at the spot where I now was seated.

Oh, what a lovely spot I found myself sitting in. I named the beautiful stream *Rapid River*, and drew out my birch-bark chart and sketched and located it. I felt that this would be my home; and could anything be more beautiful. As I sat upon a large stone near the river this is what I saw round about me. To the westward, I knew that just around the bend, but concealed from my eyes as I sat, was the long, beautiful beach of Stillwater Cove, with its inland glades that I had just passed over; to the northward and eastward, a gradually ascending grade of land, covered with lovely groves of trees in full foliage; on both sides of the river a beautiful valley of some quarter of a mile in extent, covered with a natural turf and fringed at its circumference with these beautiful groves; farther to the right a mountain that seemed of considerable magnitude. Birds passed me in their flight from one portion of the grove to the other, and I distinguished the wild pigeon and wood-dove and several others that were familiar to my eye. I observed that they came to one of the upper falls to drink, and after enjoying to the full the beautiful scenery round about me, I followed them there and tried to get a shot with my bow. I found that I could get quite near to them, say within twelve or fourteen yards, but I fired many times before I was successful enough to kill one, and even then I should not have been able to have succeeded if it were not for the innumerable number that came to drink and replace those whom I frightened away by my repeated bad marksmanship. Each shot, however, improved me, and I had also a determination to become skilled, and therefore studied and discovered the error of each shot, and improved upon it by the next. Looking down upon the terminus of Stillwater Cove from this upper fall was superb; there it lay, a pure basin of white sand, with this mountain stream dashing into it. Having feasted my eyes, I got out my flint and steel and built me a nice fire in a short time without any difficulty, and soon had my pigeon roasting at the end of a long stick over the blaze. He eat so very nicely that I took to my bow again, and after a few shots killed another, which I devoured in the same way. I found that the air and exercise and my wanderings here and there had made me very hungry, and I added to the roast pigeons several of the boiled eggs and a long draught of pure water from the running river at my feet. Having feasted abundantly, I arose, and leaving my heavy powder canister of water behind me, I crossed Rapid River just below the lower falls, and found myself on the further side of Stillwater Cove. I turned to the left and walked towards the Breakwater, and soon found myself heading for the place where the boat had first struck on the reef, and opposite to my late residence. Upon arrival there I could look across to my little hut, but I kept on till I came to the end of the Breakwater and to Point Deliverance. As I walked along the Breakwater I noticed on the inner side large masses of mussels nearly a foot in length, larger than anything of the kind I had ever seen before, the shells of which would make capital dishes. I stored the fact in my memory for use hereafter. I stood at last upon Point Deliverance and looked out to sea, but no sign of any friendly vessel met my eyes. I turned to the westward and saw a large bay, formed by my island, at least three miles across and three or four deep, bounded on the northwestern side by a slight promontory, which I concluded not to name, from the distance at which I now stood, and on account of the uncertainty of what lay behind it, now not to be seen from my present position; and as I was determined to pass round the whole island I knew that I should come to it in due season. The bay before me, into which Stillwater Cove poured its waters, I named *Perseverance Bay*, and marked the same upon my birch-bark chart. Having gazed about me and seen nothing to examine further, I retraced my steps to Rapid River, and again sat down at the upper fall, refreshing myself with a good long pull at the pure water. I started up the gorge and penetrated for about a mile into the interior of the island, and found that the river became smoother and more level as I advanced, and that the groves of trees in places receded, leaving meadows of grass, and long vistas often, on each bank. I made on this trip of a mile or so several discoveries, the most important of which was that there were plenty of goats upon the island, for I started several herds, one numbering as large as ten or twelve, from the long grass of the bottom land. This convinced me that years must have passed since they had been put upon the island, as they were evidently very numerous. I saw also a great many terrapin, or land tortoises, and saw in them a luxury for the future. I felt convinced that sea turtle would not often come to my island on account of its southerly position and climate, and I looked upon the one I had captured as an exceptional case; still, further in the summer they might be more plenty, their presence would prove my theory correct about the mildness of the climate, and I hoped it might prove true on every account.

ROAST PIGEON.—Page 91.

In the pure limpid waters of Rapid River I saw several fish darting about, some of which I was convinced were similar to brook trout, but I had not fine enough fishing gear to try for them. In the long grass of the meadow, near the bushes on the border, I started a veritable bevy of quail,—or such I took them to be, and I had known the bird well in boyhood,—and when they flushed and whirled into the air a feather would have knocked me down. My nerves were, however, getting stronger and stronger, for I reasoned that no human being could be on the island and allow such a paradise as this to remain uninhabited. I recognized amongst the trees, pines, hemlocks, maples, elms, oaks, etc.; and amongst the bushes and plants several with which I was familiar. On one of the smooth reaches of the river, passing from the meadow to higher and firmer ground, I disturbed a large flock of ducks. On the left bank of the river, which was not wooded, I came upon what I believed to be a joyful discovery for me, namely, the tobacco plant. I was not sure, but I had seen the weed growing in Virginia, and I felt sure that, although stunted, and dispersed here and there, this was the veritable article. I determined at my earliest opportunity to test some of it by curing it, and in fact plucked a small portion of the leaves for that purpose and thrust it into my bag. The taste in the green state confirmed me in my opinion, and I felt sure I was right. This discovery would be a great solace to me in my loneliness, and I felt very thankful for it.

I crossed the river by wading and jumping from stone to stone, and descended it on the other side, still seeking for new discoveries. My friends the goats were often disturbed by me, and I saw with pleasure that they were very numerous. They were, however, very shy, and ran away with great speed and evident fright, and gave me no opportunity to shoot at them. It was on this side of the river that I made the discovery that gave me bread, or rather something in lieu of it. I noticed a running vine upon the ground, and my memory told me that it resembled that of the sweet potato. I pounced upon it, and, plucking up the root, held in my hand the evidently half-grown bulb that I was in search of. It had not yet matured, but it was bread for all future time. I felt that I held in my hand the sweet potato of Virginia and the Carolinas. This set me to thinking again, Was this nature or man? Who had planted these two things, tobacco and potatoes, that I so much desired, God or man! I felt that I should never know. The shades of evening were by this time beginning to fall around me, and I made my way back to the second fall on Rapid River and arranged for the night, gathered wood for my fire, and grass for my couch, which I placed under the overhanging and low branches of a cedar, similar to the one near my hut, which I concluded to call the *Landing Place*, and so marked it upon my chart. I was pleased with my explorations so far, and foresaw that I could gather everything about me in the way of comfort that a man could desire, except that one great instinct of our nature, companionship with our fellow men. I ate my supper of turtle steaks and eggs with great satisfaction, and by the light of my fire sought my humble couch and slumber.

CHAPTER X.

Exploration of the island: Second day. Find coal and sulphur, seals, more turtles, gulls, etc.

THE next morning the sun rose with his customary brilliancy and brought to poor me another beautiful day. I arose from my hard and humble couch, and raked apart the ashes of my last evening's fire, and put on some new wood and soon had a cheerful blaze. I stepped down to the river and soon with my bow and arrows had two or three of my wild pigeons despatched, which I quickly plucked and soon had roasting over my fire. So far I had been more successful than I could have hoped to have been; no savages, no noxious or deadly animals, but all a seeming paradise. I soon finished my simple repast, and strapping my canister upon my back and taking my harpoon in hand I commenced my pilgrimage round about the island, which I was determined to accomplish before I undertook any other task.

I passed across Rapid River and pressed towards the sea coast and finally, after a walk of about a mile in a northeasterly direction, came out upon a bold shore with quite a promontory on my right hand. How wistfully I looked out upon the ocean, the day being so clear that I could see to a great distance; but my view encountered no welcome sail,—only the everlasting waste of waters spread out before me. With one long sigh of repining at my fate, I passed on to the right and commenced ascending the promontory before me. I trudged on through open land and small groves of trees till I arrived at the summit, which was barren and gave me a great view seaward and convinced me that I was on the extreme northeastern extremity of my island; for I could see nothing to the northward of me, but in my rear and to the eastward I saw another projection extending into the sea, to the southward of which I could not observe. From my elevation I was able to see somewhat of the interior of the island, and this was what met my view: to the south of me and at about two miles distance, as I should judge, I saw quite an elevation, and far away to the southwest another large hill, almost a miniature mountain. The island seemed well wooded in all directions and presented a beautiful appearance in the brilliant morning sun and pure clear air. I looked long and anxiously to the eastward for land, but saw nothing: and my friends the goats seemed to have deserted me in this part of the island, for I saw no signs of them. I turned to pass to the southward and eastward along the coast-line, when I was attracted by the appearance of the ground round about me, having in seams amongst the rocks a dark appearance. I stooped down and by the aid of my knife broke off some portions of this familiar looking substance, when lo and behold! I held in my hand veritable anthracite or bituminous coal,—I was not expert enough to know which, although I thought it to be the former. What a discovery was this for me, and yet what a natural one, after all. I could not rest satisfied with my own convictions that it was really coal that I held in my hand; but then and there drew out my flint and steel and started a wood fire, at which I had become expert, and digging up large fragments with my harpoon and knife, which I took care not to break or dull in the operation, I cast them upon the flame. Yes, it was true past peradventure,—I had found coal, veritable coal, that burned readily in the midst of my wood fire where I had piled it in the glowing embers and flames. Every once in a while it seemed to give off quick jets of flame, and this led me to examine the specimens before me more carefully to ascertain the cause. And upon breaking open, with a stone, quite a large fragment, I saw within it a large broad streak, as wide as my finger, of a yellowish cast, which I instantly recognized as sulphur, and in fact my memory told me that the coal received from the island of Formosa, in China, especially from the surface collections, abounded in sulphur, sometimes so much so as to be disagreeable for house use. But one thought flashed into my mind upon this discovery, matches! matches! matches! Yes, here was before me the foundation of all lucifer matches, and I had only to consult, on my return, my Compendium of Useful Arts and Sciences, to avail myself of it and find out how to combine it with the other necessary articles to have real *bonâ fide* matches. I was overwhelmed with joy, and blessed the hour that had been so fruitful in comforts for me, should I have to remain upon this island.

I went to work and soon had sufficient of crude sulphur or brimstone—I do not know which it should correctly be called—to answer all my purposes for experiment, and carefully wrapping it up in some leaves and fastening it with a thread of my manilla, I placed it in my bag. I thought how rapidly my fortunes were changing: here had I within a few hours insured myself against cold and loss of fire by the few gifts of nature laid at my feet. I tried, in spite of my miserable solitude, to be thankful. Before leaving the promontory I drew out my birch-bark chart and named the point *East Signal Point*, as it was evidently a capital place at some future day to erect a signal of some kind upon, being high, bold, and barren, and overlooking the surrounding country. The place where I had found the coal and sulphur, I simply named the *Coal Mine*.

Having marked these carefully down, I rolled up my chart and took my way towards the easterly cape to the southward of where I stood. After a walk of about a mile and a half, I found myself upon what was evidently the extreme eastern end of my island, not nearly so high as East Signal Point, but well elevated and barren towards the sea, backed with a thick forest inland. Standing on this point, which I named *Eastern Cape*, I saw that this was the limit of my island in this direction, and by figuring in my head and looking at my chart I estimated that I was about six miles from my landing-place in a direct line, and about eight by the coast line.

I saw nothing here to attract my attention except many seals on the southerly shore, which was now opened to my view for the first time. On the broken and jagged rocks of this coast-line I saw great numbers of these animals of different sizes, and I should think of different species.

It being by this time about noon by the sun, I sat down and opened my bag and regaled myself upon turtle steaks and cold boiled eggs, for I did not go to the trouble of lighting any fire; this, washed down with water from Rapid River in my tin canister, formed my frugal meal. Towards the southwest I saw trending a long sandy beach similar to the one inside the breakwater, except that this was lashed by the long regular billows of the ocean without any intervening barrier. After taking a good long rest, I got upon my feet and started again upon my journey. I soon came down upon the hard sea sand from my elevation, and the seals that I had seen from above seemed little inclined to move at my approach, and I passed quite near to several amongst the rocks before reaching the beach. No one can credit what pleasure I experienced in simply observing these poor dumb creatures so near me, with their great, beautiful black eyes, and I lingered near them for over an hour, so fascinated was I by them; they seemed almost like companions to me, so subdued and lonely had I become for want of the society of my fellow-creatures, even in these few days. I talked to them, and they answered me by snorts of surprise, and by gazing at me with their great staring eyes. I would not have hurt one of them for all the wealth of the world, and when I left them I took off my clumsy hat and bid them good-by as I would intelligent beings.

After leaving the seals behind me I became despondent again, and cursed my cruel fate. My loneliness rushed upon me with renewed force; however, I tried hard to thrust it from me, and before I had made a mile upon the beach was in better spirits again. I saw flying round about me several birds that I recognized as gulls, and ahead of me a turtle made his way into the sea, but I made no attempt to stop him, having plenty of food and to spare, but I was glad to see that my expectations, or rather desires, were more than fulfilled, and that my capture upon the other side of the island had not been an exceptional one, and I could look to this creature also for food; but that question, as well as the one of water and fire, was fast disappearing from my mind, as the certainty of providing all easily was being hourly forced upon me. I foresaw that I should not want for any of these things, that I should, with a little care and labor, have comforts undreamed of when I first found myself cast on shore.

The question of savages even was fast being settled, for I reasoned that I could not have made such a distance round about the island without finding some traces of human beings, if there were any upon the island; still I cannot say that all my nervousness was gone, I was yet too lonely, depressed, and solitary, and knew yet too little of the whole island, to have recovered all my usual and natural evenness of temperament; but I was improving, and my head was already filled with ideas of boats, balloons, and I know not what, in which I was in some way yet to escape. After walking about three miles along this lovely beach I came, upon turning a slight elevation, to the mouth of a small trickling brook not over three feet wide, which found its way to the ocean from a background of forest trees. I sat down by the side of it, and soon ascertained that the water was pure, cool, and fresh. I almost smiled at the fury with which I had attacked this problem of water upon my first arrival upon the island; but on the other hand I felt pleased to think that I had also overcome it, and had made Nature serve me. I took quite a rest at this point, and, after sauntering about, concluded, as the sun was sinking towards the west, to make it my resting-place for the night. For this purpose I went a little further back from the beach under the trees, and carried up there large quantities of good dry seaweed, and made me a nice comfortable bed, lighted a good fire, and after a quite good supper of my eggs and turtle steak, which I warmed in the ashes and roasted over the hot coals, I took out my pipe and tobacco to smoke and meditate. With the precious weed that I drew from my pocket I mixed a small quantity of the wild weed that I had found, and having of course had no time to cure it I first shrivelled it up over my hot embers and then mixed it with my tobacco. By the scent and fragrance whilst it was being dried in this manner, I had no longer any doubt but what I had found the veritable article, and when I came to mix it in my pipe I felt convinced.

It being early, and feeling that I surely had a supply of this luxury, I indulged in a second pipe-full, and whilst I was puffing away I was also trying to look into the future. My remembrance of the original Robinson Crusoe was that he was a bungler at anything and everything that he undertook, whilst I felt that I was a good mechanic, thoroughly versed in the use of all tools, and especially in working in iron; that I had a fair, sound, common-school education, and that I had been ingenious and inventive both on sea and land from my boyhood; that I had had good experience in navigation and seamanship, and intercourse with many nations; that I knew, and had acquired, the little every-day habits of many curious people, and that I had seen numerous ways of doing the same things in different parts of the world. Besides all this I had a valuable book which would serve me in the very points in which I was deficient, and I felt that with it I could do thousands of things that the old Robinson Crusoe never dreamed of doing. I felt that if there was iron to be found in the island there would practically be no end to the improvements and comforts that I could gather about me; with tools of iron and steel, with my knowledge of mechanics, what I could not make would almost be the question.

I felt convinced that there must be iron upon the island, even if not in large quantities, enough for my purpose if I could only find it. I knew that the Japanese islands had plenty of it, that Formosa and New Zealand abounded in it, and I was determined to find it if it was to be found.

I had already made up my mind to move to Rapid River for my home, unless future discoveries showed me a different state of affairs in the western part of the island than I expected to find.

I wondered, as I sat, whether my famous lamp tower was performing its duties during my absence, but it did not trouble me any longer even if it were not, for I found that my flint, steel, and tinder were all-sufficient for my purpose, and was I not soon going to make real matches?

Sitting smoking, and revolving all these thoughts in my mind, I saw the sun sink into the western ocean, and shortly after wrapped myself up in my seaweed covering, under the shelter of a bunch of low shrubs, and dropped asleep.

CHAPTER XI.

Exploration of the island. Third day. Stalking goats. Mirror lake and river and bay. Sad moonlight thoughts.

I AWOKE to still another pleasant day, having scarcely moved in my seaweed bed during the night. My first duty was to make my way to the running brook and have a good wash, and then to look about me for breakfast. I bethought myself all at once of the turtle that I had seen on the beach the previous day, and I made my way back to the place where I observed the marks of its ingress into the sea, and, looking about carefully, I soon found its eggs nicely covered up in the sand. I took as many as I wanted and turned about and made my way back to camp, and soon had them roasting in the ashes.

After breakfast I pushed my way a little into the island, and found pleasant groves and fields, in one of the latter of which I observed a flock of goats feeding. They did not see me, and I found by the direction of the wind that I was to leeward of them, and therefore beyond their scent, and I determined to stalk them, or creep in upon them, and try to get a shot with my arrows. For this purpose I divested myself of all extra articles, and, armed only with my bow and two arrows, and my knife in its sheath, I got upon my hands and knees and commenced the task. At first this was not difficult, for the animals were at least two hundred yards distant from me, and by taking advantage of different clumps of trees and shrubs I soon approached within one hundred yards of them; but then my labors commenced. I felt that I must get very near to be sure of my aim with arrows, and to pierce them sufficiently deep to produce death; at least within twenty-five yards.

I made progress for some twenty or thirty yards quite well by keeping within range of intervening objects, but when I found myself within about sixty or seventy yards of them I found my task difficult, and I had often to lie upon my belly and drag myself along, inch by inch, so as not to be seen, and with one hand to clear the ground before me of the smallest twig or anything that would make the slightest noise when my body was passing over it. It took me a full hour to make twenty-five yards in this manner, which brought me within, as I should judge, thirty-five yards of them. Here my precautions had to be increased, and it was with infinite labor, and the expenditure of at least another hour (but what was time to me) before I found myself behind a low clump of bushes, on the other side of which, not more than twenty yards distant, I could hear the goats feeding. Silently I fitted an arrow to the string, and rising inch by inch till the muscles of my arms and thighs were nearly worn out from immovability, I saw through the thin tops of the bushes one of the goats not fifteen paces from me. I was at a fever heat of excitement, and drawing my arrow silently to the head, and with the utmost force of my arm, I launched it at the game, and saw it pierce the goat through and through, who fell upon his side, but immediately regaining his feet made off with amazing swiftness; its companions, to the number of some six or eight, scattering in all directions. I followed as fast as possible on foot, and saw with satisfaction that my game had not gone more than one hundred yards before it began to waver and to lose its speed, and within the next fifty yards, in the open field, to fall upon its side, and, just before I arrived, expire, in its fall breaking the arrow short off. I looked down upon the creature with exultation, for it was food, and good food, and I had won it by honest and persevering labor, and by means of what in our day was considered a contemptible weapon.

I took out my knife and cut the creature's throat and let the blood escape, and then taking him—for it was a buck—by the hind-legs I threw him over my back and started for my camp on the rivulet, where I dumped him down beside my fire and commenced to skin him. This, with my knife, I soon completed, and, cutting off some of the tender chops I soon had them roasting on the coals, for, although I had breakfasted a few hours before, I could not resist the temptation of tasting fresh meat, which, on account of my sea voyage, it was so long since I had enjoyed. I found it exceedingly good in flavor, but a little tough, my customer evidently being far from young. He carried a very handsome pair of curved horns, and a long, majestic beard. The hair was of rather a finer texture than I expected to find it, and was not very long or thick; another proof, I thought, of my theory of the mildness of the climate. The animal was such a true, commonplace goat, such as one sees on whalers, that I felt convinced that the breed had at some long-distant day been left on the island in this manner, but no signs had I yet found of the island having ever been lived upon or explored. Then, again, it might with great probability have been stocked fifty or sixty years ago, and any signs of persons having been here, except they had left enduring monuments of some kind, would long ago have been effaced or destroyed. I made up my mind to accept the blessing without puzzling my brains any more to find out how it happened that they were here. I was pained to know what to do with the large mass of flesh that I had remaining, and having, at Buenos Ayres, seen the jerked beef of the prairies, I cut large portions of this creature into strips and hung it on the surrounding trees and bushes to dry and cure in the pure air. A large portion of what was left I roasted and put in my bag, throwing away the remainder of the turtle steaks and gulls' eggs, of which I had become somewhat tired. All this brought me to the afternoon, and, packing up all my articles, after a good long smoke, harpoon in hand I started forth again, heading towards the westward.

Two miles' walk brought me to an elevation running out into the sea, which was evidently the southern extremity of my island, and I marked it upon the chart *South Cape*, and the hill-top *Watch Hill*, for the reason that I could see from this position much further in both an easterly and westerly direction than from any point upon the island that I had yet reached.

To the right of me as I faced to the southward was a beautiful and lovely bay, at least a mile and a half deep and three-quarters wide, as smooth as glass, in which the shadows of the surrounding shores and hill-tops were pictured. I marked it down upon my chart as *Mirror Bay*. Long and steadily I looked to the southward before leaving South Cape, but no sign of land met my longing view. To the westward, on the other side of Mirror Bay, trended the white sand beach, backed by groves of beautiful trees which were in full verdure. Drinking in all the beauties of Nature round about me, I turned my steps towards the head of Mirror Bay, and in about a mile and a half came to a river of considerable size pouring into it, which seemed of some depth, and was at least thirty or forty yards wide. I followed this stream about a mile and a half more, when, struggling along by the side of the river, which I named *Mirror River*, through a short undergrowth of a sort of scrub oak, I all at once came out upon the most lovely lake imaginable, fringed round about by beautiful groves of trees, and looking like molten lead or silver in its quietness and calm. I named it at once *Mirror Lake*, but in forcing my way to its margin, after having for a few moments enjoyed its beauties, I started up from its borders innumerable flocks of birds, amongst which I distinguished geese, swans, ducks, and other birds of which I knew not the name. I sat down upon the borders of this beautiful sheet of water and contemplated it in silence.

After having enjoyed its beauties to my fill, I passed again to the river bank to pass over and get again to the seaside, but I found the water rapid and quite deep, although not over my head, and I was obliged to undress and carry my things over one by one, and to make several trips before I stood with all my weapons round about me on the southwestern bank. This lake I should say was about one mile in extent and half a mile wide, of nearly an oval form, and its waters, which I tasted and found excellent, singularly pure and limpid, with hard, sandy shores, and free from any slime or stagnant water. A walk of a mile brought me again to the seaside, and I trudged on, I should judge, about three miles, till I saw a ledge of rocks jutting into the sea and confining my vision as to the extent of the island in that direction. As I drew nearer I saw forms upon the rocks that looked like human figures,—like soldiers in full uniform,—but singularly small in size. For just one moment I was deceived,—nay, even frightened,—but the next my sailor's eyes told me they were penguins, and sure enough, as I approached, my soldiers gravely plunged into the ocean and swam out seaward. I named the point, *Penguin Point*, being the first of these birds that I had seen. From this point the coast ran in a northerly direction in almost a straight line, but I had no time to examine it further on this day, for the beautiful sun was fast dipping into the western ocean before my eyes, with nothing to veil the magnificent sight. Eagerly did I look for land as its lower limb touched the water and set it all in a blaze, but nothing met my view.

I did not find here the thick, shady trees of the remainder of the island; but short, stumpy cedars and pines, and I noticed that the land was flat and sandy. I built a small fire so as to light my pipe and enjoy its company, and gathered together my customary bed of seaweed. The stars came out in all their brilliancy, and by and by the moon came creeping up behind me over the island, but I could not sleep as usual. I was too solitary and desolate to enjoy that luxury of forgetfulness, and I sat for long hours into the night, listening to sounds that, in any but a sailor's ear, would have created fear and anxiety; for on the ocean side I heard the never-ending pulsations and throbs of its ceaseless breathing, and inland the nameless noises of the night which I had learned years before in anchor-watches in some distant river of a far-off clime. I was not afraid, but I was lonely, and in the agony of my spirit I prayed for rescue from my living tomb; but better feelings came to my mind as the night wore on, and I thought over how much I had to be thankful for, and how many comforts I could get round about me with a little industry and foresight. I suppose that it was about midnight when I put out my pipe and fell asleep; at any rate, when I awoke it was broad daylight, and the sun at least two hours high.

CHAPTER XII.

Exploration of the island: Fourth day. Finish the exploration of the island, and build stone house at Rapid River.

I SOON had my fire in a blaze and my breakfast despatched, and started forward on my explorations. As I advanced, I saw that I was on a smooth, hard sand-beach, with a scanty growth of cedars and pines on my right hand inland. After walking a few miles I turned to the right and walked inland, expecting, from the formation of the land, that the part of the island I was upon could not be very wide; and sure enough, after a short half mile through the stunted cedars, I came out upon Perseverance Bay, and within plain sight of Point Deliverance and Stillwater Cove, some three miles distant. I found that I was upon a narrow tongue of land which formed the western boundary of Perseverance Bay and ended in the promontory that I had seen from Point Deliverance in looking across the bay on the first day of my explorations.

I did not consider it worth while to pass back again to the west shore, but kept along on the beach on the margin of Perseverance Bay towards the point to the northward. In a mile or two more I reached it, and found that it consisted of quite a sandy elevation, covered with stunted cedars, and evidently the extreme northern point of my island. I named it *West Signal Point*. Here I sat down and took a review of my situation. I had virtually made the circuit of the island; for from where I sat I could see the margin of Perseverance Bay, which, if I followed, would end in landing me at the mouth of Stillwater Cove, near my hut.

I saw that my task was completed, and that I was alone on my island, the only living human being, the latter-day Robinson Crusoe. My feelings were those of joy and grief,—joy, that it had pleased Providence to keep me out of the hands of savages, where I could pass my life in peace, if it was so willed; grief, that I should be forced to this lonely and solitary life. I sat many hours at this spot, thinking over plans for the future, and what I should do to make myself comfortable and protected from wind and weather, and from future enemies, should any ever visit me. On the whole, I found my mind much relieved at the positive proof that I had of the island being uninhabited, and when I arose and started for home it was with a freer step and lighter heart than I had had since my landing.

A trudge of about seven miles, as near as I could judge, brought me to Stillwater Cove without adventure of any kind, although I passed many objects in the way of birds, trees, and vegetables that were of intense interest to me. From thence, a walk of about a mile brought me to my hut at about five o'clock by the sun, hungry and tired, but perfectly well and strong. Convinced as I was of the utter solitude of the island, still it was with care and almost awe that I approached my hut, almost expecting to see some strange creature, either human or savage, within its walls. Nothing met my ear or eye. Quietness and solitude reigned, and everything was exactly as I had left it. I examined my lamp tower, and found that two of the lights had gone out, I suppose on account of the wick, but the others were burning well but dimly. I immediately gave matters here my attention, and soon had all to rights and "ship-shape." I had even a feeling of comfort as if I had arrived home, and I went about the matter of getting supper and starting my fire with a cheerful feeling; and whilst doing so I caught myself at one time quietly humming an old sea ditty.

I saw plainly that my residence at this point was at an end, and that Rapid River was the place for me to make my home. So I took little care to arrange matters about me on this evening, but sat down in a matter-of-fact way and ate my supper, whilst the sun was sinking into the west; but when night came on, with my pipe as a solace, I thought of everything, and these are a few of the thousand and one things that coursed through my mind. I gathered together the following facts:—

First. That the island was uninhabited, fruitful, and fertile, abounding in everything that could conduce to my comfort; pure fresh water in several localities, birds and fishes of many varieties, goats, trees of all sizes and growth, tobacco and sweet potatoes, coal and sulphur; an evidently mild and even climate, and many useful things, no doubt, which I had not yet discovered in my hasty circuit of it.

Second. That I was the only living soul upon it, and that all these natural treasures were mine to avail myself of by industry, ingenuity, and perseverance.

Such being the facts of the case, what should be my future course, and what my plans and duty? Amongst the many that flashed through my mind, I picked out these, as forming the most important to first receive my attention.

First. To erect a strong, serviceable habitation at Rapid River, which I had already in my mind concluded to call the *Hermitage.*

Second. To ascertain at as early a day as possible, by the best means at my service, and by the assistance of my "Bowditch's Navigator," the latitude and longitude of my island, as near as I could come at it.

Third. To project a chart from the "Epitome," and find out how far I was from other lands.

Fourth. To never desist from seeking for iron ore at every opportunity, for with that I could do almost anything.

Fifth. To study out some way of building a boat, of size and strength, without the use of iron or timbers to strengthen her.

Sixth. To take the greatest care of my seeds, and watch with the utmost solicitude those which I had planted.

Seventh. To capture at as early a date as possible one or two of the wild goats, so as to be able to breed up tame ones for my use.

Eighth. To procure at once some kind of ink, and keep up my journal and reckoning on birch-bark leaves.

These were amongst the first tasks that my brain gave my body to execute, and although thousands of others ran through my head, they all more or less depended upon the consummation of these cardinal ones. At a late hour I sought my seaweed couch in my hut, and fell asleep. The next morning I commenced work in earnest. I had my idea about ink (which, if my memory served me right, the old Robinson Crusoe had so much difficulty about and was unable to make), and wending my way to the beach of Stillwater Cove, with my harpoon in hand, I waded in, and commenced looking carefully for squid or cuttle-fish, feeling positive that the ground was too good for them not to be found there, having seen them frequently lying dead in the seaweed whilst passing around the island.

I had not long to hunt before I saw several on the pure white sand before me at the bottom of the water, about the usual size of those at home, say some six inches in length, but when I attempted to strike one with the harpoon it darted out of the way, backwards, just as they used to do in my boyhood days, ejecting at the same time the fluid from his body which I desired to preserve. I saw that it was useless to try and get any of these in deep water, and therefore waded ashore and commenced looking for them in the numerous shallow pools that the receding tide had left near the margin of the water, and I was successful in finding five nice fellows embayed in a small, shallow pool, not six feet in circumference, whence I had no difficulty in kicking them out upon the sand, opening them with my knife, and pouring the contents of their dark fluid (which is the sepia of commerce) into a deep mussel-shell. I had the foundation for good ink, and with the addition of a little water, and a quill made from the feathers of my friends the gulls, I was easily fitted out with pens, ink, and birch-bark, which was all I needed for many a long day to come.

This task ended, and a trial made of my new ink by making some notes and entries of my doings up to this time, I commenced upon another, and that was the building of the Hermitage at Rapid River. I selected a beautiful spot a short distance below the fall, the noise of which was delightful to my ears, and laid out the foundations for my future residence. I was at least three weeks preparing all the materials for the building of the same, passing over each day to my task and back to the hut to sleep. I was determined that my future residence should be strong and well built, and able to withstand the action of wind and rain, and for this purpose I passed my time in gathering large masses of clam and oyster shells, and reducing them to lime by the action of fire. This was long and laborious work, but I needed lime to make mortar, and I could only get it in this way. I also wanted some hair to mix into my mortar, and this puzzled me for a day or two, but I bethought me of the goat's skin that I had brought home with me from near Mirror Lake, and I at once put it to soak in one of the large sea-oyster shells in water impregnated with wood ashes and some of my lime to make the hair come off, which it readily did after a few days. I then went about, whilst burning my shells for lime, to capture some more of the goats, and by means of numerous snares made of my manilla rope, and placed in the localities that I found they frequented, I had no difficulty in capturing as many as I desired, all of which I killed and cut the flesh into narrow strips and cured it in the air for future use. The lye in which I soaked the skins gave me the hair for my mortar, and the skins remaining, although not tanned in a proper sense, were useful to me in a thousand ways.

When I had gotten together a sufficient quantity of lime, hair, and nice dry sand, and an immense pile of the largest stones that I could move, I commenced to build my house.

I marked out a parallelogram of what I should judge by my eyes to be about twelve feet in width by eighteen feet in length, and upon these staked-out lines I dug a trench some three feet in depth, and into it I pushed my heaviest stones for the foundations, taking care to place particularly large and smooth ones at the corners.

Luckily building material was plenty and at no great distance. Rocks of all sizes were to be found at the base of the rocky point that was just below me on Stillwater Cove. Of course I used much larger stones than I could lift, which I got to where I wanted them, and into place, by means of small rollers, which were sections of quite large tree-limbs, that I had cut off with infinite care and patience with my knife, into the requisite length, and large, strong stakes of wood, made in the same manner, which I used as crowbars, or as we sailors should call them, and more properly, handspikes. After my first tier was laid round about the whole trench, I rolled in other stones on top, putting mortar between them before I pried them into place. When the trench was filled I commenced to use smaller stones, but still ones that were quite large and almost unmanageable; and as the walls got higher, I had to content myself with stones that I could lift with my hands. But then, again, I at this point commenced to double my wall, using two stones side by side where I had formerly at the base used one. In this way my house, gradually, after some three months' incessant labor, began to take shape. On the front, sides, and rear, at proper distances and height, I inserted large timbers so as to form windows. These timbers, which were often as large as my thigh, I obtained by finding dead trees that would suit my purpose in the woods, and burning them off at the proper length, so that I could handle them. Of course a foot or two or a burned end was of no consequence, as it was laid upon the wall in a horizontal position, and mortared into its place with the stones that were piled upon it. In this way I formed rough but strong uprights and cross-pieces for my door and windows, all of them firmly built into the wall, and forming part of the solid walls themselves.

BUILDING THE STONE HUT.—P<small>AGE</small> 120.

At the end of some three months, after incessant and exhaustive labor, I had the satisfaction of seeing the stone work to my house all done, the top of the walls being at least two feet above my head, and I should say at least twelve inches thick; this was all mortared up both on the outside and inside, and was as strong as a fort. The last layers of stone gave me the most trouble, but by means of a large, nearly round stone, upon which I stood, I was enabled to finish my task, although at great pains. The erection of the roof was comparatively an easier matter, although that also took me a long time and was only completed after great patience. I found growing on the shores of Rapid River a species of cane, and I found that I could cut these down without difficulty, and gathering a large number of them, I spliced them together for my uprights and ridge-pole, with manilla yarns, and then laid the remainder close together from the ridge-pole to the eaves, projecting over the latter some two feet. These were secured to the ridge-pole by manilla strands, and in the

73

centre of my house a strong forked tree as large as my leg received the ridge-pole from both ends of the house, and sustained it. This cane roofing, which was both light and strong, I thatched heavily with sedge, similar to that with which I had covered my hut. I fastened up the openings that I had left for windows with goat skins for the present, hanging them on wooden pegs which I could remove when the weather was fine. At the rear end of my house I had, I should have said, built me a nice open fire-place and a tall chimney, which I had had to finish after the roof was done, so as to stand upon the latter to carry the chimney up high enough to make it safe to carry away the sparks from my thatch. Into this large, dry, airy, and clean room, I brought by different trips all my worldly goods. I had put out the lamps in the tower at the landing-place hut long ago, having no further need of it, but I still kept it as a receptacle for my spare flint, steel, and tinder, and knew that I could go there to obtain them to start a fire should I by chance be without them on my own person.

Whilst my house was in course of construction I had not been idle about a thousand and one other things, but I had let nothing of importance interfere with this—to me—imperative duty. After my house was all finished I commenced setting out round about it, at about fifty paces distant, a species of alder, which I noticed grew rapidly and thickly, and which I foresaw would in a very few years entirely conceal my habitation. When I had gotten things well about me, I found by my journal that I was in the month of March,—in other words, that the summer had passed and that I had been none too soon in preparing myself for the winter, which was yet to visit me.

CHAPTER XIII.

Make a hatchet of my iron hammer. Make matches and utensils for house. Team of goats, chairs, table, etc. Birch-bark canoe. Arrangements for winter.

I HAVE said that when the Hermitage was finished the summer had passed away. Let me describe what the weather had been, and something concerning the climate and fruits and plants that had been coming to maturity, whilst I was hard at work on my house.

I found the summer days often hot, but never very unpleasantly so. I experienced the usual amount of rainy weather that it would be natural to find in a similar latitude in the northern hemisphere. There were days, of course, in which it was very hot, and there were other days in which large quantities of rain fell, but upon the whole the climate was delightful, more like that of the inland sea in southern Japan than anything else to which I can compare it. The island was singularly free from fogs and mists, but then I might reasonably look for these later in the season. When the day was very sultry, I had always the beautiful sandy basin of Stillwater Cove to bathe in. So far I had nothing to complain of on this score, and felt confident that the winter would be mild and short. It was about this time that I felt the need of more tools, and especially a hatchet, which I finally concluded to make out of my hammer, which, be it remembered, I had constructed out of the boat's anchor. I took this hammer, and by repeated heatings and beating with a piece of the remaining shank, I forged it into the shape of a hatchet, still leaving the eye as it was when used for a hammer. I then went to the place where I had been cast on shore, and procured some clay like that from which I had made my lamp tower, and formed some rough crucibles by burning them in hot wood fires. Into one of these I put my hatchet-head and filled round about it with small pieces of charcoal and slips of the skin of my goats and small pieces of unburned, soft wood, and carefully sealed up the orifice with a quantity of the moist clay, and cast the crucible into a hot fire; not hot enough to fuse the iron, however, and kept it there, watching it carefully from time to time, nearly three days, when I dragged it out of the flames, broke open the crucible, and took out my hatchet-head, converted into excellent steel of superior hardness and temper. I soon procured a soft species of stone as a whetstone, and by the labor of a few hours brought the edge to a fine degree of sharpness, and, having fitted a handle by means of my knife, I had a splendid instrument to aid me. No mortal ever looked upon the works of his own hands with more admiration than did I upon my steel hatchet. Many things which I had not before deemed possible I could now attempt. After I had made my hatchet I commenced many improvements round about me. I made several trips to my vegetable garden, and saw with the utmost satisfaction that all my seeds had sprouted, and I supplied myself with all kinds of vegetables during the whole season. I took great care to preserve carefully a great plenty of the seeds of each species, and thought more of that than enjoying them, but they were so plenty that I had ample of nearly all for food. My wheat, however, I saved every kernel of for sowing next year.

I had by this time several very tame goats tied up about the hermitage, and I made up my mind to break a span or two of them to harness, and for this purpose, as I could not construct wheels, I made a sled by bending two small limbs in the shape I desired, and fastening them by cross pieces, all of which I held together by straps of manilla lashings and by holes burned with a hot nail from one part into the other, into which I drove small pegs of hard, seasoned wood, and finally turned out quite a respectable sled, about twice as large as a common boy's sled, and the runners much wider, so as not to sink into the soil. To this I attached my four goats, making the harness out of the hides of those that I had killed, which I sewed together in good shape with strong manilla twine by means of my bradawl, making real good, strong work. The traces I made by laying up small strands of the manilla rope, and ended by turning out four sets of breast-plate harnesses; strong and durable, and easily adjusted.

I found very little difficulty in breaking my team into drawing this sled, and by means of it I brought home many useful acquisitions for my winter's use, but chiefly coal from my coal mine, which was about two miles distant. I used to carry my sled across Rapid River, below the falls, and then drive over my team upon a sort of rocky causeway that I had built so that they did not have to tread very deep in the water, and then, harnessing them up, I used to start for the mine, and by means of the anchor-fluke, I dug out easily enough coal in a short time to load my sled, and dragged it home to the river, whence I transported it across in a basket of willow twigs that I had made in my leisure moments. In this way, before winter, I had at least two tons of coal near the door-way of the hermitage, all handy for winter use. With this same sled and team, I gathered also a large amount of wood, which I could now cut into proper lengths with my hatchet. I constructed of small stones and mortar in one side of my large fire-place, a sort of grate, with a chimney made of sections of pottery pipe manufactured of clay from the landing place, that led up into the main chimney, in which I could burn my coal if I wished to, or make a wood fire beside it. I found very little difficulty in making several clumsy but useful vessels of clay, which I baked successfully and glazed with salt; my book of useful arts and sciences giving me an idea how to do it. My next task was to make matches, and the information necessary for this I also procured from my book. The wood I easily obtained by splitting up small, thin sections of well-seasoned pine with my hatchet, and these again I sub-divided into matches with my knife. I then caught a quantity of fish with my harpoon, which I had no difficulty in doing at any time, especially the small dog-shark species, and chopped up the bones of the head with my hatchet, placing them at a distance from my habitation. These I allowed to putrify till they were luminous with phosphorus, which I gathered carefully in the night-timc by separating it from the putrid mass and carefully pressing it. I then procured some turpentine from the resinous trees near to me, and made a mixture of sulphur, phosphorus, and turpentine, which I heated, and into which I dipped each match singly, and laid it aside to dry. I afterwards dipped each into a melted solution of pure spruce gum, very thin, to preserve them from the weather. I made several attempts before I was successful, but at last I obtained the right proportions and made me a stock of matches that worked well if they were used with care, and if the weather was not too damp, when I was often driven to the use of my flint and steel. For winter provisions I visited, with my sled and team, the sweet-potato fields, and laid in a large stock, also picking a quantity of the tobacco plant and curing it for my own use, and this was my greatest solace in my loneliness.

I found upon the island a species of gourd, and I soon had in my home a set of these useful utensils, which, by dividing, I also made into bowls and saucers. I also, from Breakwater ledge, procured any number of the large deep mussel-shells, nearly a foot in length, which were useful as receptacles for all sorts of things.

I found no difficulty, by a treatment which I found in my book, in preserving, by means of tannin procured from the inner bark of a species of scrub oak with which the island abounded, all the skins of my goats, and I soon gathered together a stock of both tanned and untanned ones, some with the hair on and some with it removed. I hated to attack my friends the seals, and yet it was about this time that I made a trip across the island and killed ten of them for the purpose of procuring their skins, which I added to my stock.

I found no difficulty, by means of my knife, in cutting out quite a respectable pair of trousers, and a sort of hunting jacket from the goat-skins; but the sewing of them together was a harder task. Still, before winter set in, I was clothed in quite a nice buckskin suit, and had, with my seal-skins and goat-skins with the hair left on, the withal to make at any time a winter suit that would protect me from the cold, so that I had that trouble off my mind. As for shoes, I easily made me a pair of moccasins of the goat-skin, with the hair side within, which were very comfortable and useful. I also from my skins made me a much more useful and ornamental cap to replace the one of rushes that I had worn throughout the summer.

I also made me a nice tobacco pouch, and several other useful articles of skin, including a sort of game bag, which I carried over my shoulder by a broad skin band; this latter was especially useful to me. I also made from my clay several useful but rather clumsy pipe-heads, and with a reed stem I was fitted on this score and had no more fears about breaking my old clay one. For meat for the winter I laid in large stocks of my dried or jerked goat's flesh, and I had little fears on this score, as I could always procure fresh meat now, when I desired it, for my goats had begun to propagate already. From them I already obtained milk, in larger quantities than I had any use for, but had too many things to think of, of more importance than to try at this time to make cheese. I caught in the river large quantities of a species of herring, and also a few fine salmon, which visited the river, but only for a short time, being unable to ascend the falls. All of these I cured by smoking, by building a hut round about them and keeping them for a long time in the densest smoke by burning green wood underneath them. I cured also in this way some few hams of my goats.

After having gotten these things about me, I tackled others of less importance, perhaps, but necessary for my comfort. In one of my excursions to the coal-mine I discovered what I felt convinced was limestone, and upon bringing a piece home, and testing it by fire, I found I was correct, so here I had all the lime I should ever need for any purpose, easily procured by burning the stone and gathering up the residue. I now commenced upon the interior of my house, and in the first place made myself a nice hammock of four goat-skins, with the hair inside, which I stretched from the central post of my room to one of the window jambs. I then went to work upon a bed, and cut first with my hatchet four uprights with forked ends, like the letter Y, from as many limbs, about four inches in diameter and three feet high; into these forks I placed two long poles, some two inches in diameter, and fastened them there securely by means of manilla strands. I then braced the ends and sides by lashing, both lengthwise and endwise, poles about one foot from the ground, which kept the whole in shape, and although it was not so strong as if dovetailed together by a cabinet-maker, it answered all purposes, and when pushed up against the wall, in the corner, was further supported upon two sides. Across this I stretched cords of manilla, and over them I laid long, soft, pliable rushes, and over them again seal-skins, with the hair side upward; and I had at last a capital bed. My chairs did not give me so much trouble, for I found two old roots of trees, that, with a little hacking off here and there with my hatchet and a goat skin for a seat, made as easy chairs as any body ever sat in; of course they were too heavy to be moved about, but for all practical purposes they were perfect, and I could rest in them with the greatest comfort and ease.

With my clay I easily baked some shallow dishes with a handle, into which I poured my sharks' liver oil and fitted with pith wick and had no want of light. One of these lamps I suspended from the ridgepole in nearly the centre of the room, just clear of the upright, and two or three feet above my head, fitted with three wicks, which, when lit at night gave me a pleasant and abundant light. I made favorites of one or two of my young goats, and used to allow them to occupy the house with me, and became much attached to them, and in the evening when not too busy, amused myself by teaching them to walk on their hind legs, and other playful tricks which seemed for a moment to make me forget my loneliness. I was not satisfied with what I had yet done for the interior of my house, and I therefore went to work, and made myself a table on the same plan as the bed, except that it was higher and much lighter, and across this I stretched a large section of birch bark which I stripped from a tree; this table pleased me so much that I went to work and made a lighter one still for my ink, pens, and books, etc., retaining the other for eating purposes. In fact, before the winter was ended I had four of these tables in the house, which were very handy, and yet after all were not difficult to make. For a door, I cut several canes and lashed them together with manilla rope strands, and hung it by the same material, but it would not open or shut very well, and I was forced to lift it carefully, but then I only closed and opened it once a day, morning and night. The floor of my house troubled me more than anything else, but finally I covered it with a coating of clay that I brought on the sled by repeated trips to the clay field; this I mixed with a quantity of lime and sand and put it down whilst moist, and it formed a sort of cement, and soon became hard and firm, but it was always dusty to a degree and not as clean as I could have wished, but it did very well,—at least, I could think of nothing to improve it.

It was at this time, when I seemed to have gotten everything well about me for the winter, which was sensibly approaching, for it was now the month of May, and some of the days had been quite chilly and unpleasant, that I was taken with the insane idea of building a boat. I do not know for what earthly purpose I desired one, except, possibly, I might coast along in Stillwater Cove or the margin of Perseverance Bay and if I found anything that I needed I could transport it better in the boat than any other way. I was well aware that I had no tools to make a boat with, but for that very reason I was determined to make one. I had made up my mind, if I must play the part of Robinson Crusoe, that I would at least prove to myself, if to no one else, that thousands of things can be accomplished by a little ingenuity and contrivance that seem difficult upon first view. For instance, I thought at once of several ways in which I could make a boat: one, by hollowing out a log with my hatchet and by means of fire; another by making a light frame of twigs and stretching skins over it; or still another and very much the best method, by taking the bark from a birch tree and making an Indian birch-bark canoe. This latter was the easiest and simplest, and a plan that I knew something about, so I went about in the woods till I found a splendid great birch that pleased my eye, some two feet or more in diameter, with a bark seemingly without a flaw. It took me nearly a day to build up a kind of platform of wood and stones, so as to reach high enough up the trunk of the tree to make a circular incision with my knife at about fifteen feet from the ground, and then one perpendicular till within about two feet of the ground, where I made another round about the tree, leaving me a strip of bark some thirteen feet in length. This I forced off, using great care not to tear or split it, by means of a series of wedges which I forced in under the bark with my hatchet. At last the piece lay before me upon the ground, and the worst part of my task was done, for I soon brought the ends together, filling them first with melted pitch, and lashed them with thin withes of a kind of willow which I split for the purpose, the same as the Indians do; and having sewed and lashed up both ends, after cutting the bark with my knife in the right shape, I split up with my hatchet long, limber, thin pieces of a species of ash, in the green state, something like hoops to a flour barrel, but somewhat wider and stronger, and with these cut in different lengths, and inserted within the bark, I gave the canoe its shape, the longest, widest, and strongest ones being in the centre, from which they shortened towards each end. Inside of the gunwale the whole length on each side I stretched a pliable cane pole, rolling the bark round about it and sewing the whole down with manilla strands and green withes of willow.

It was amazing to see what a beautiful, light, and graceful boat I had produced with only about a week's labor; one that I could put upon my head and carry towards the water with ease. I soon, by means of my hatchet and knife, fashioned out a paddle, and my canoe was complete. I launched her in Stillwater Cove, and she floated like a duck, and was besides of a beautiful model, and, as I well knew, would stand terrific weather if properly handled, being one of the best sea-boats in the world, not excepting the famous Nantucket whale-boats. I was delighted with my success.

I did not gather all these things about me without many bitter hours of loneliness and despair; but their constructions and the reading of my book, which I consulted almost nightly, kept me often from miserable repinings. I felt that I was gaining, and that I had not yet done making nature, ingenuity, and industry improve my condition and increase my comforts.

CHAPTER XIV.

Make chairs, and arrange my house, seal-skins, and goat-skins. Provide provisions for winter. Discover wild grapes, and make wine and vinegar. Find potassium, or saltpetre. Make gunpowder, and by means of my compass discover iron. Thoughts of the future.

THE completion of my canoe, which I named the "Fairy," was a great delight to me, and I made several trips in her along the coast in Stillwater Cove, and made an exploration near the place where I had first landed. Somewhat into the interior of the island, I came upon what was a great discovery for me,— although I had the seeds amongst my stores, and had already planted some,— and that was grapes, in large and abundant clusters, growing wild and naturally. Here was both food and drink for me, and they were at this time in their prime. From them I could make vinegar, wine, and raisins. I gathered a large quantity, which I placed in the canoe and transported to the Hermitage, and although late in season hung up many bunches to dry in the still quite warm sun, and from the remainder I extracted the juice by pressing them between my hands and catching the liquor in several of my numerous earthen jars. The flavor of these grapes was a little wild, but pleasant and agreeable. I knew that fermentation would take place, and that in time I should have a light claret wine, and thereafter good wine vinegar. To cause fermentation, and to improve the flavor, I put a piece of goat's flesh into each vessel, and covered up the mouths with earthen covers that I had made to each.

I was no longer in any fear about expending my manilla rope, for I had some time since begun to use strips of rawhide of the goats skins for lashings, than which nothing could be better, and I also cut many skins into very fine strips after they were tanned, which served me for smaller strings, and even thread for rough sewing. For finer sewing I often used the sinews of these creatures, and I had by this time converted several of my nails into steel, after having pierced them with an eye, and by grinding them down and polishing them upon stones I had made several very good sail-needles, which were extremely useful, and it was a small matter to make a "palm," or sailor's thimble, from the skin of a goat, to go upon the right hand, to force the needle through any material, exactly the same as is done by sailors in all their stitching and sail-making. In place of the little round thimble fixed into the centre of the palm, to receive the head of the needle in pushing, I inserted a flint-stone with a roughened surface, which answered the purpose very well, and I could now do all kinds of rough sewing without the use of my awl, which had been a slow and laborious manner of proceeding. From this time forth I had no difficulty in sewing my jackets and trousers with strong sinews, which held them firmly together in the seams. It is scarcely credible how many things I gathered around about me that were useful as well as ornamental.

Before I had done completely furnishing my house I set about making me a movable chair, as well as the easy ones that I had made of old roots, and this I did by means of my hatchet. I procured four smooth limbs of trees, two of which were about four feet in length and two about one foot six inches. The latter were to serve as the front legs, the former as the back legs and also the back of the chair. These limbs were about two inches in diameter, as I did not wish the chair to be heavy, but light and portable. Into all these uprights I bored holes at proper distances by means of my anchor shank, heated to a red heat, which I thrust through them, and cutting smaller round limbs for rungs I forced them into the holes made by the hot iron, and soon had the skeleton of a nice light chair made to my hand. I was so pleased with it that I set about another immediately, and soon had it also finished. It was not at all a difficult job for a mechanic. For the seat of these chairs, upon one I wove rushes thick and strong, and upon the other I laced a fine piece of seal skin with the fur left on. They were both useful and comfortable, but rather straight in the back, like the old ancestral chairs that I used to see in the attics in Vermont.

I had got tired by this time shooting at the wild pigeons with my arrows, and found no difficulty in capturing all I wanted by means of snares, made from the hair of my goats, which I set at the watering-place whenever I wanted any of them for food, and gave over firing ten or fifteen shots before I could kill one, when I could capture a dozen in an hour should I need them.

I took down my goat-skins at the windows and replaced them by thin skins of the same animal, almost parchment, which gave some light through them, and fastened them up with thorns, driven into the wood, for the winter, the open door giving me, with their subdued light, enough to see by so as to perform all the work that I wanted to inside, and when night came I had my lamps in full blast, for oil cost me nothing.

I made, before winter set in, several excursions, in all directions, and especially one in the direction of the mountain that lay upon my right hand, only about a mile from the Hermitage, when I went to the coal-mine. This mountain I made up my mind to ascend, and see if I could not make some new discovery. I fought my way up its steep sides till I had arrived at nearly one-half the distance, apparently, from its summit, when I was halted by the appearance of a small brook that trickled past my feet. I noticed that the water and the stones were both of a brown, rusty color, and it flashed upon me that it must be caused by iron. If I could only find that substance I thought that I could be almost happy, even in my solitude. What could I not do with that metal to aid me? the handling of it would be to me child's play. I could make of it cast-steel, and of cast-steel all manner of tools by means of moulds. This working in iron had been my trade, and I had no occasion to consult my book to know how to avail myself of it should I be so fortunate as to find it. I followed this little trickling brook, not over six inches wide, till it branched into two smaller ones, and, still following the smaller one, traced it till I came to a place where, in a bubbling spring, the water issued from the mountain's side. The discoloration of all the stones near me proved to me that I was near iron, and that the mountain whence the tiny streams issued contained it; but in how large masses I could not judge.

I left my little stream and looked about me carefully, to the right and left, for I did not want to pierce the mountain whence the water issued, as I wanted a dryer spot to make my explorations, and knew that if there was iron it would be found near by the brook as well as in the exact spot whence the spring burst forth. I finally, at a little distance to the left hand and rather down the hill, found a place that looked as if it might prove a good locality to prosecute my search. The ground was covered with boulders, of different sizes, and there was quite an opening on the mountain side, the undergrowth being only shrubs and plants, with the trees and groves below me in larger groups. In this opening I set to work, turning over such boulders as I could lift, and there were many that by aid of a handspike, cut from a sapling with my hatchet, I was able to remove and send bounding down the mountain side. I scratched into the side of the mountain in this way till I had made quite a little excavation, but I was obliged to give it up and return home for my pickaxe, as I called my anchor-fluke, and with this instrument, and carrying my dinner with me, I attacked the mountain the next day and made more progress. After working some little, in an irregular way, into the mountain side,—for I had to avoid the heavier boulders and solid stone,—I came upon a crystallized mass between two rocks that seemed to be exuding from the mountain side. It looked something like common salt, and I put some of it in my mouth to see if I could recognize what it was by the taste. It had hardly reached my palate before I sank down upon the earth where I stood, with the excitement of the knowledge of the discovery that I felt sure I had made. My sense of taste told me plainly that I had found saltpetre, and saltpetre meant *gunpowder*! GUNPOWDER! and gunpowder meant strength to protect myself with and power to blow the mountain to atoms to come at my iron should nature try to resist me by enfolding it concealed in its bosom. I grasped my pickaxe and picked out quite a lump of my precious discovery, and started hastily for home.

It was too late to do much on that day, as my usual household cares and the milking of my goats and getting supper took up most of my time; besides I wanted to consult my book as to the proportions in which to mix my ingredients to make gunpowder. I knew nearly the right proportions, and felt confident that I could get it exactly by repeated experiment, but I also knew that my book would give it to me exactly and save me much loss of time in this direction. I knew also that willow or alder made the best charcoal for gunpowder, and, thank God, there was no lack of these trees upon the island. If I obtained gunpowder I could make some kind of a gun, for I knew that, in ancient history, cannon even had been made of *leather*, and fired repeatedly without bursting. I could certainly make a tube of some kind, so strongly reinforced with skin and twine and raw hide, that it would stand the discharge of a small quantity of powder without bursting, and if I found iron I would soon solve all the difficulties about a gun barrel, let me once get hold of the raw material in any quantity.

A thought struck me in this connection. I would soon prove whether there was iron in the mountain side by taking my compass there on the next trip, and seeing if it was drawn from the true north towards the mountain side, and if so, in what direction: this would tell me how to dig towards my treasure, and not waste time by going in any wrong direction. This seemed a happy thought, and I was jubilant over having conceived it. The only thing that I did to help things along for the morrow was to pick out carefully, from my wood-fire ashes, small pieces of charcoal that I thought would serve my purpose, and to pick off from several pieces of my coal a quantity of sulphur all ready for my experiments. The next morning I set to work in good earnest, and having discovered the proportions in which to add my different ingredients, I soon had the pulverized charcoal, sulphur, and saltpetre together, and then, moistening the mass slightly, I kneaded them together till they were completely incorporated. I then, by a slow heat, dried my gunpowder cake upon hot stones that I heated at the fire and then carried to a distance, first carefully dusting them, and placed my gunpowder paste upon them in an earthen jar to be dried. As my cake was not very large, I was not very many hours in doing this; and as I knew that I ought not to use any iron or stone in pulverizing the mass, whilst this was going on, I procured a smooth rolling-pin made from the round branch of a tree, and smoothed quite a surface on the upper side of a large fallen tree with my hatchet, so that I had a sort of table to roll my powder upon. Again, to prevent all accidents, when my cake was thoroughly dry, I carried it bit by bit, having broken it by a blow of my wooden rolling-pin, to my fallen-tree table, where I crushed it under the roller, putting pieces no larger than my thumb-nail under the roller at one time, so if there should be an explosion, it would be on so small a scale that it would not injure me in the least, should it take place. As fast as this small amount was pulverized, I carried it again to a distance and placed it in a gourd for safe keeping, but I pulverized very little before I interrupted my task to rush with quite a handful to my fire, and, taking a pinch, I cast it into the flame, and, puff, puff, puff, it ignited as it struck the fire, just as the particles used to do in my boyhood days. Even this did not, however, satisfy me. I laid the rest down upon the floor, and standing at a distance with a coal in one end of a cleft stick, touched it, when it exploded as quickly and completely as any ever turned out by any mill. One more proof and I would be convinced. I ran and got from the sea-shore one of the large shells for which I have no name, but which I had formerly used as lamp reservoirs, and going to my powder table, soon pulverized enough to pour a handful into it, and to close up the lips with moist clay, except one orifice; to this I laid a piece of manilla soaked in the dampened powder as a slow match, and having set fire to the same, and retired to a safe distance, I awaited the result. It seemed an eternity before the slow match burned to the orifice, but when I had almost given up hope, in one instant, with a loud report, the sea-shell was burst into a thousand fragments. I was successful; power and strength were added to my resources. I lay down upon the sand by the sea-shore where I had retired to watch the explosion, and fell into a brown study, which enwrapped me, body and soul, for many hours, till I was called to myself again by the decreasing light of the setting sun. The next day I sallied forth, armed with my compass, for the mountain side, and upon arrival I noted the direction of the magnetic north by my compass, the card of which I had released from its packing and set upon its pivot. Having carefully ascertained this, I entered the small hole that I had made in the mountain side, and held the compass in several places against the earth, when the needle turned perceptibly away from the magnetic north and pointed in towards the interior of the mountain, and by several experiments I found out in just what direction I ought to advance, and by the attraction of the needle I felt sure that the ore, which I now was convinced was there, could not be very far distant from where I stood, and that one large blast would lay it open to me. I therefore went to work and gathered quite a quantity of the saltpetre and started for home to make my gunpowder for the blast that was to open up to me my long-sought treasure, valuable to me far beyond any other metal on this earth in the circumstances in which I was placed.

In five days' time I found myself in possession of over twenty pounds, I should judge, of good gunpowder. I found by my book that it was not at all peculiar to find potassium as I had found mine, and further, that to purify it I needed to mix it with equal parts of wood-ashes, and then add water and allow it to stand a few hours, and then draw off the lye and place it for three days in the sun, in shallow vessels, to evaporate, and then boil down what was left, to procure absolutely pure saltpetre, all of which I did. And when I had manufactured my powder, and observed by experiment that it was much sharper and louder in explosions than before, showing the improvement of purifying the saltpetre, I placed the whole lot in my goatskin bag and started for the mountain. Arriving at my excavation, I looked about to see what I could do to make my explosion effectual and do the most good. By examination, I found that there was quite a space between the two inner boulders that obstructed my way, and a sort of vent-hole that led, I knew not where. Into this I commenced to pour my powder, and used up over two-thirds of all I possessed before I saw any result. Finally, the crevice, just as I began to despair and thought I had thrown away and lost it all, showed that it was full by refusing to receive any more. As soon as I noticed this, I knew that I had an excellent chance to make a good blast, and I therefore pushed in the powder in sight, and was able, by shoving it downwards, to add at least two pounds more. I then carefully inserted a strand of manilla previously soaked in wet powder, and dried, into the mouth of this crevice, and well down into the powder; I then stuffed the whole with small pebbles and moist earth, and finally placed quite a large rock against the vent, and, with a prayer for success I lighted the fuse and retired to a safe distance to watch the effect. As before, it seemed as if it would never ignite, and I waited and waited, taking care to be well distant and well sheltered behind a large boulder, till finally, with a dull, low, smothered noise, the charge exploded. I was disappointed, and was afraid that my powder was too weak or ill-made, but when I arrived at the spot I was amazed at the execution that had taken place: the whole roof had been uplifted and thrown open, and the boulders that had resisted my further entrance cast to one side, and the whole side of the mountain pierced and opened in a wonderful manner. I dashed into the opening that had been made, and the first fragment that my hand closed upon was pure iron ore. I was like one mad with joy. I acted as insanely as I had once or twice before since landing upon the island, and danced and sang, and ended by sitting down and bursting into tears. Upon further examination I was inclined to believe that the whole mountain was composed of iron, and that I only needed to pierce the crust in any direction to get the precious metal. My discovery lay just about one mile from my home, and quite accessible.

I found that the blast had brought to view quite a large surface, on one side, of my saltpetre, whilst further to the southward appeared the iron ore in masses that I could pry out with my pickaxe. After having feasted my eyes long enough upon my treasure, I started down the mountain, smoothing the pathway wherever it was rough, and opening up a way for my team and sled to bring down the ore to the hermitage.

I absolutely saw no end to the improvements that I could make now that I had iron to work with. I could do anything within reason, and make anything I chose to make. A thousand and one schemes of escape by its means rose up before me. If at this moment I could have had the companionship of my fellow-kind, I should, I think, have been unable to ask any blessing to be added to my lot. Here was I in evidently one of the finest climates of the earth, with everything about me even now to sustain life, and with many of its luxuries, and with the foundation laid for many more.

Upon a close examination of the specimen that I had brought away with me in my bag, home to the Hermitage, and by consultation with my book, I felt convinced that I had discovered what is called magnetic iron; that is, iron ore that is most universally dispersed over the earth. The action of the compass added to this belief, and the limestone formation was exactly fitted to this kind of ore, which is the same as is generally called the Swedish iron ore, one of the best-known irons in the world. The color was a sort of black iron shade, and the ore brittle and attracted by the magnet of my compass; whereas, if my iron ore had been hematite it would have been of a dull steel color, and probably without magnetic properties.

How I revelled in what I was going to do. First, I was to build my kiln and put the ore through that to purify it of sulphur, arsenic, water, &c., then to a blast furnace, to be heated with a flux of limestone and coal, and in the melted form run into pigs in the sand of the smelting-room. Once in this melted form I could make, from moulds, chisels, axes, hatchets, plane-irons, and saws, by a treatment of the melted iron ore. By means of blasts of cold air I could change the whole mass into Bessemer steel. With the tools I have named, in my hand, I could go to work at once to erect a sawmill on Rapid River, near the Hermitage, and with the greatest ease saw out all the plank I should want for any purpose under the sun. Then my thoughts strayed away to nautical instruments, some kind of a quadrant, then the latitude and longitude of my island, and then a chart on Mercator's projection from my Epitome; and then turning-lathes, iron boats, electric wire, gunmaking, steam engine and propeller boat, torpedoes for defence, and all the means to escape from this miserable solitude. All these things, I say, ran through my head like wildfire. Nothing was now impossible. I had got my genie, and I was determined to make him work. The weather was getting cooler and cooler, and one or two storms had already warned me of the approach of winter. The leaves began to fall, and the whole island commenced to look dreary and forsaken; the grass, however, retained its freshness in a remarkable degree.

It was in the latter part of May that I discovered my iron ore, and I knew that this was the same month comparatively as November would be in the northern hemisphere; and although there had as yet been no actual frost, much less any ice or snow, yet I saw signs, not to be disregarded, that the weather would be more severe and colder before the spring days would come, and yet evidently I had not much to fear from a very great degree of cold, as my theory concerning the climate had so far been singularly correct. I commenced, therefore, at once, without loss of time, to collect my ore by means of my team of goats, and transport it from the mountain to Rapid River. I did not bring it over as I had the coal, for I determined to erect my blast furnace and kiln on the further side, and opposite to my home, as being more convenient in many respects.

I worked hard myself, and worked my team hard, in bringing to Rapid River both the iron ore and coal, and also quite a large quantity of the potassium, which I carefully took into the hermitage till I should need it to make more powder. It did not take very many trips, however, after all, to get the iron ore that I should use during the winter, at least, but the coal to smelt it took me longer. After I had gathered all of each that I thought I should need I gave my goats a rest, and set to work to make arrangements for my smelting-furnace, kiln, and smelting-room, and how I proceeded I will now go on to relate.

CHAPTER XV.

Make a mould for bricks. Build a brick-kiln and make bricks. Build a smelting-house, blast-furnace, kiln for cleansing ore. Meditations. Build water-wheel and fan-wheel, and set my machinery for an air-blast to reduce the ore.

In the first place I went to work, and with my knife and hatchet fashioned out two quite smooth pieces of wood about four feet long, three inches wide, and perhaps one inch thick. I smoothed these on one side with a great deal of care, and finished them off by means of dry shark's skin, which stood me admirably in place of sandpaper. I placed these two slips of wood parallel to each other, about four inches apart, and fastened them in that position by means of blocks of wood of the same size and thickness, placed between them at equal distances of about six inches, which subdivided the whole into eight equal compartments, fastening the cross-pieces in by means of hardwood pegs driven into holes in the side, made by a red-hot nail. When my labor was finished my affair looked like a set of pigeon holes, such as are used in an office, except they were open on both sides and had no back, and each compartment was four inches wide, three inches deep, and six inches long. This was an insignificant looking thing in itself, and, except the smoothing of the inside in all parts, was not a labor of any great magnitude, and yet by means of this instrument I intended to make a great stride forward in civilization. The thing that I had made was a press or mould for bricks. I do not know the technical name, but I knew that if I placed this instrument upon the level hewn side of any fallen tree for a table, and filled each compartment with clay properly moistened, I should at each filling and emptying turn out eight equal-sized, unburned bricks, all ready for the kiln.

To enable me to prosecute this work I moved for a few days to the landing-place, where clay in abundance was to be found, and where my old hut would give me shelter. When I say I moved there for a few days I should say that I came home to the Hermitage every second day to care for my flock of goats and look after my household cares. Upon my arrival at the clay pits I soon set to work, and my clay was so pure that I had little trouble in moulding it; and, after having fixed a smooth plane upon a fallen tree as a table for the bottom of my mould, by levelling the same with my hatchet, smoothing with my knife, and finishing with my shark-skin sandpaper, I set to work moulding, getting my water at a short distance inland from a boggy piece of ground abounding in springs, which existed right under my nose, a little to the left, when I was so anxiously distilling water upon my first arrival at this very spot. I transported this water, by means of gourds and my canister, easily, to the clay pits, and soon had a fine array of bricks, the moulding being simple, and I found I could work quite fast; and by means of my knife and a sharp clam-shell or two, and with a large mussel-shell for a shovel, I had no difficulty in filling the mould quickly and trimming off all superfluous clay very rapidly. As fast as I finished one set I dashed the mould over with fresh water, so that the next lot moulded would slip out easily after being carefully pressed in. As fast as I made the bricks I allowed them to lie for a day or two in the air till they hardened, and then commenced to pile them up in shape to be burned and perfected into bricks. As a boy I had often examined brick-kilns, and I knew that I must make, or rather leave, a sort of oven under them, and, throughout the whole pile, apertures through which the flames and heat would penetrate so as to bake the whole mass. I built my kiln with care and on the above principles, and in less than a week had a goodly array of bricks all built up in complete form. I then with my goat team drew to the kiln all the old dead wood I could manage, and with my hatchet cut it into suitable lengths to be thrust into my ovens, for I had three of them in the whole pile, and with great glee set fire to them all one evening, and saw that they had a good draft and burned fiercely. I worked like ten men to keep these fires perpetually going, and, prepared as I had been in the commencement by laying in a large supply, I, with the aid of the team of goats, was able to keep up with them and feed them regularly. I do not remember now how many days I burned these bricks, but it was very easy to examine them and see when they were sufficiently hardened and burned; and when they suited my eye, and I experimented upon several by breaking them open, I let the fires gradually go down, and found myself in possession of a nice stack of bricks, fit for any purpose. These, as they cooled, I transported in the canoe to the landing opposite to the Hermitage, where I had determined to arrange all my appurtenances for smelting the iron ore.

In the first place I commenced a house or workshop, about twenty feet long and twenty wide, by building up walls of stone, as I had done for my Hermitage, but in a much rougher and coarser manner, without foundations, and very much lower, not over six feet in height. Over this I erected the usual bamboo roof and rushes for thatch, with one opening for a window, and one for an entrance, in opposite sides. The floor of this room I covered with pure white sea-sand for one half, and the other half with soft, pulverized, dry, clayey loam that would do me for castings. In one end of this smelting-house, as I called it, with the feeding-place outside, I built, in an aperture in the wall left for that purpose, a solid blast furnace of my bricks, which I lined with my pottery cement, and made in every way complete to receive the ore and smelt it. This was to me, except the manual labor, boy's play. The opening for the fused iron was within the smelting-house, and I could run the ore on to the sandy floor in channels made for that purpose, and thus procure my pig iron or Bessemer steel as the case might be. In this blast-furnace I left several channels to be connected in some way with a blast of cold air, for without this blast I could not of course expect to smelt the ore. To improve the draught, and to have Nature help me all possible, I built the chimney or cone of the blast furnace at least twenty feet high, of bricks, tapering the same in a cone form from the base to the apex. I worked upon this matter like a beaver, and felt well satisfied with my work when it was done. My smelting-house stood quite near to Rapid River Falls on the further side, for I had foreseen that I should have to use some power to get up speed to move some kind of a fan wheel, and I knew that I could only do it by means of water, and had therefore, for that very reason, placed the house near to the bank and had built the blast-furnace on the end of the house nearest the river.

After finishing my blast-furnace completely I left it to dry and harden, and set to work at my roasting-kiln, on which my ore was to be first purified and cleansed. This was comparatively an easy affair, and was made wholly of bricks, underneath which large fires could be built, and through the numerous interstices the flame would reach the ore placed upon the bed above; the flame, after passing through and over the ore, to be carried out at the other end of the bed by means of a brick chimney about twelve feet in height, high enough to give a good draught.

As soon as I had my kiln done I commenced drying it by lighting a fire under it, and found that it had a good draught and would answer my purpose admirably. I then went to work again with my team of goats, and dragged near to the smelting-house all the dead wood—and there were large quantities of it —that I could lay hands upon, that was anyway near or convenient. Being now in the month of June, I found the mornings often quite snappishly cold, and was glad of a little fire often in my home. But I worked so hard in these days that I scarcely had time, after finishing my supper, to smoke a pipe of tobacco before I was ready to throw myself upon my seal-skin bed and fall asleep. In these times I worked so hard and persistently that I often cooked enough corned meat to last me a week at a time, and could always draw upon my stores of salted fish and smoked salmon, and goats' hams, vegetables, etc., whenever I needed them. Of course many days I was unable to work in the open air on account of rain and storms. Those were the times that I took to improve my clothing, patch up my moccasins, and make up warm skins for the cold weather; look after my little flock of goats, which often strayed away short distances, but by being careful to feed them each night regularly on a little delicacy of some kind, mostly sweet potatoes, they always came back to the shelter of a nice warm shed that I had constructed for them near my home, made on exactly the same principle as my hut at the landing-place.

It would take too long to enumerate the various little articles that I had gathered around about me, and how perfectly my mind was at rest on the following subjects: First, that I could not suffer for want of food, for I had enough and to spare of everything; amongst many others the following principal ones,—dried goats' flesh, jerked goats' flesh, smoked goats' flesh, smoked goats' hams, wild pigeons, eggs, fresh fish for the catching, smoked and salted herring and salmon, sweet potatoes, cabbages, turnips, beets, etc., vinegar, wine, salt, milk, etc. Second, that I had a large quantity of nice skins, both cured and uncured, of seals and goats, to last me a lifetime; with fuel, light, and covering against all contingencies, and tobacco for my solace. Third, that I felt confident and perfectly satisfied that the island was uninhabited and unknown, and I went to sleep each night without fear of being interrupted on the next day. My nerves had wholly regained their tone, and I was grown strong, rugged, and hearty, whilst my experiments with my iron ore and my hard work upon the smelting-house gave me the necessary incentives to keep me from thinking of my own sad fate. I saw such a future before me, could I have iron in all its forms ready to my hand, that I was kept in a state of excitement just right for my temperament, and was restrained thereby from gnawing at my own heart with bitter regrets which would avail me nothing. I do not mean to say that I did not have bitter and dreadful moments of despair and utter hopelessness, but these occurred usually in the evening when I felt my loneliness the greater than when I was at work in the open air. But I began to dispel this even by giving another current to my thoughts, making my pet goats go through their little series of tricks to amuse me and draw me away from myself. A good smoke at my pipe, and a glass of quite fair claret wine used often at these times to freshen me up and dispel my mournful thoughts. When these would not work I used to seek oblivion from my thoughts by plunging into my "Epitome" and studying out some problem that would aid me in, at some future day, fixing the latitude of my island, or else amused myself by reading something from my book of useful arts and sciences that might be of service to me some time.

Up to this season of the year no snow had as yet fallen, but ice had skimmed the little fresh-water pools outside of the main river, and some few nights had been cold outside; but, thanks to God who had been so merciful to me, I was warmly clothed and housed, and had nothing to fear from wind or weather.

During some of the stormy days I puzzled over the problem of how I was to get blasts of air forced into my furnace. And this is how I did it eventually. I cleared away a small portion of the fall of Rapid River, so that the water rushed with great force through a sort of flume of about four feet in width and three feet deep. I secured and regulated this floor by means of a series of gates and pieces of wood that I drove into the soil on either side. I procured them by cutting a tree, about twelve inches in diameter, into sections of about five feet in length with my hatchet, by infinite labor, and splitting them with hard-wood wedges into long rough clapboarding or scantling about an inch thick and I had no time to smooth them, but had to use them as they came to hand, rough from being split with the wedges; but as the wood was straight-grained I got quite a quantity of very fair pieces of board that suited my purpose, although not smoothed. I drove these, as I have said, into each side of the flume in the dam to protect the sides from being washed away, and arranged a sort of gate so as to keep all water from passing through when I so desired. It was a bungling sort of a job, and not very strong, but answered my present purposes quite well. I then went to work upon my water-wheel, which I intended to hang in this flume, and, by opening the gate above, allow the water to flow down upon it with great force and turn it, so as to obtain motion, and power to which to connect pulleys and wheels on the land side upon the axle of the wheel. I studied long over the formation of this wheel, and finally constructed it by taking for the axle a smooth, strong limb of a hard-wood tree, about four inches in diameter, and apparently perfectly circular in form. From this I stripped the bark, polished it with shark's skin, and cut it off so as to leave it about seven feet in length. I then, by means of rawhide and willow withes, fastened, at right angles to this axle, light but strong arms made of cane, extending about three feet in each direction from the main axle. These I again strengthened by means of crosspieces parallel to the main axle, which I bound across the arms, and over these again lighter canes yet, crossing the whole fabric from the extremity of one arm to the base of another, till I had a framework of a wheel, light and fragile to be sure, but very tough and well bound together, and each withe and rawhide string set well taut and securely fastened in real sailor style,—and sailors can make immensely strong articles bound together only with string, the secret being that they know how to make each turn do its work, and how to fasten the whole securely. I sunk into the ground on each side of the flume a strong post of wood some eight inches in diameter, each ending at the top in two natural branches, or a crotch, like the letter Y, which I smoothed out by means of my knife and fire so as to receive the axle of my wheel and allow it to revolve in them. These posts I set in the ground very deep and very securely, and battered down stones around their foundation, and braced them also with other stakes driven into the ground near to them, at an angle, and lashed securely to them. Upon my framework of the wheel I tied on, with rawhides, slats or "buckets," as they are called, of my split clapboarding, to be acted upon by the water and cause the wheel to revolve. Outside the axle, upon the shore side, I fitted a wheel of cane, about three feet in diameter, constructed in the same way as the main wheel, but not more than six inches in width. This was to receive a belt to communicate the power and motion of the water-wheel to a series of pullies that I was yet to make. After getting the wheel in place, and the axle set in the crotches of the two uprights, I opened my gateway and saw with pleasure that it revolved very rapidly, evenly, and with great strength. I also observed that the paddles were submerged just as they ought to be, only about a foot in the water, and that the rest of the wheel revolved in air. I also discovered that I could regulate the speed exactly by letting a larger or smaller quantity of water into the flume by means of my gate. I did not do all this without infinite detail and hard work, and it was at least a month before my wheel was completed and hung in its position. This brought me into July, and now I commenced to see ice form in the smooth pools near the river, and once, upon the fifteenth, was visited with a severe snow storm, but a day or two of pleasant weather soon carried it off. There were days also in this month when storms arose and lashed the ocean into monstrous billows, and at these times I visited the breakwater and East Signal Point and looked upon its grandeur. These were the days in which I felt blue and dispirited. But I also knew that the winter must ere this have reached its greatest severity, and although it was now really cold and everything frost-bound, yet it was not like zero weather at home. There were more mild and pleasant days than cold and unpleasant ones. There was evidently a warm current of the ocean embracing the island and keeping the climate mild. I felt confident that cold weather would soon be gone, and that I had nothing to fear on that account, for I found no difficulty in keeping myself perfectly warm at any time in the open air by a little exercise. As for my moccasins, they were warmer than any shoes I had ever worn, and my skin clothing was, even in this winter weather, uncomfortably warm, and on mild days I often used to change my sealskin coat that I had made myself for one of pliable goatskin leather without any hair upon it. My water-wheel I found was, although wonderfully light, of excellent strength, and when I constructed it I was well aware of the tough properties of the cane used in its formation, which might writhe and give, but would not break. I kept the axle down in the crotches or "journals" formed for it, by means of greased straps of rawhide, so that it could not jump upward, and yet would revolve easily without being bound or cramped. My next task was to connect my water-wheel with a series of pullies on the shore and near to the blast-furnace, so as to force a column of air into and through the ore that I intended to smelt, by means of the different channels that I had left for that purpose when building it, all of which ended or entered into one opening in the side nearest the water-wheel.

Near this opening I built, at about three feet distant, a little room completely of brick, about two feet wide and six feet high, with the narrow end pointing towards the opening in the blast-furnace that connected with all the interior air-channels that I had left when building it. This room I covered on top with flat stones firmly cemented down, and closed it up air-tight, except an opening left in the brickwork at the top, six inches in diameter. Opposite the opening into the blast-furnace, which was at the same height, and on the two sides of the structure, equidistant from the ground and the top, I left two similar holes in the brickwork, and opposite to them planted two stakes in the form of the letter Y. In other words, I constructed this building to contain a wheel similar to my water-wheel, about six feet in diameter, which was to revolve in air instead of water, and force a column into the blast-furnace. I should say that I made such a wheel with paddles and hung it in its bearings before putting on the top of flat stones or building up all around it. When completed I had a wheel enclosed in an air-tight place, the paddles of which would, when revolving, push the air into the opening left at the top of the end facing the blast-furnace. Around about the axle on each side the openings were not closed, purposely; for it was here that the machine was to suck in the air which it discharged into the blast-furnace opening by means of a tube made of goatskin which connected the two together. On the outside of the axle I built a small and very light wheel of cane, only a foot in diameter, to receive the pulley for the wheel on the axle of the water-wheel. I had only to connect these two together and my task was done. The two pulleys were distant about fifteen feet, and I had to make a band of goatskin, about three inches wide, over thirty feet in length, to connect the two. This I did by cutting strip after strip and sewing them strongly together in length till I completed my band. I had only to place this upon my pulleys, open the gate, let on the water, and the task would be finished. Having arranged everything so as to be all ready the next day, I got across the river on my stepping-stones, and went to my home to think matters over. I knew, as a mechanic, that the affair would work, and that I had much more power even than I had any need of. But I could not rest. I should not be content till on the next day I saw all the wheels, already greased and lashed into their sockets with rawhide, revolving by the mere motion of my lifting the gateway and letting on the water. I smoked and thought and paced my room for hours, and finally, when I went to bed from sheer weariness of mind and body, I passed a disturbed night. Morning saw me bright and early upon my feet, and, snatching a hasty morsel of food, I started for the smelting-house, got out my band and stretched it from pulley to pulley, and with trembling hands went to the gateway at the dam and let on the water to my undershot water-wheel. It did not hesitate a moment to obey the force of nature and the law of mechanics, and the volume of water had scarcely struck the paddles before the whole apparatus began to work, the axle to revolve, and the band to move.

OPENING THE WATER GATE.—Page 164.

I let on a very little head of water first, and rushed to my fan-wheel. There it was, moving with great rapidity, and the connecting goatskin bag was evidently distended with air. Thence I rushed to the other side of the blast-furnace, where the feeding-place for fuel was, and by casting in small, light objects saw them sucked up the chimney at once. I was successful. I had at least ten times the power that I needed for my purpose. I rushed back to the dam and cut off the water, perfectly content with the experiment without bringing any shock upon my machinery by putting on a full head of water, which I saw I did not need, as my fan-wheel, as I supposed, was turned with the utmost ease, having no resistance except the air. I could do nothing more this day but admire my handiwork, and arrange little matters here and thereto perfect the whole affair and get ready for my first smelting of the ore.

CHAPTER XVI.

Smelt my iron and make Bessemer steel and all kinds of tools. Erect an anvil and forge. Build a saw mill, and plant a farm and kitchen garden.

HAVING gotten everything all ready for my purpose, I placed, as nearly as I could judge, about a ton of the broken ore in my kiln to be roasted or calcined, and after this was accomplished, I transferred it to my blast furnace and added to the calcined ore about a ton and a half of half-burned coal, and one-third of a ton of limestone; these being the proper proportions, as I was well aware. Under this, and around it, I placed a large amount of coal fuel, and having ignited it by means of a large quantity of wood placed under the whole mass, I went, when it was well started, to my gateway on Rapid River, and set my machinery agoing, which started the fan-wheel, which immediately created a terrific blast, and the whole furnace was soon in a glow. I kept this up by feeding new fuel, till by certain signs I felt confident that the mass of ore was smelted, when I shut down my gateway so as to regulate the blast to its minimum and keep the fan-wheel just revolving. I then dug away the clay at the orifice of the blast-furnace that opened into the smelting-room, and had the supreme satisfaction of seeing the molten ore flow out like water into the furrows of sand that I had formed and excavated to receive it. I had made this furrow for a purpose also, and had something in mind when I formed the sand mould, something like a foot in depth and eighteen inches in length, exactly under the nozzle of the delivery orifice of the furnace. The molten ore ran into this rapidly and soon filled it, forming a rough block of iron a foot thick, a foot wide, and eighteen inches long. When the fiery fluid had completely filled this, I shut off the discharge by thrusting some moist clay into the orifice. This block that I had just made was to be my anvil, and as it was large and would take time to cool, I directed the orifice of the furnace to one side by means of a clay channel, so that the next discharge should not interfere with it; and as my desire was now to get steel in smaller quantities so that I could use it, I drew narrow and shallow channels through my sand at quite long distances from the blast furnace, but all coming together in one deep channel under the orifice, but spreading to different parts of the smelting house, as the ribs of a fan do from the point at which they are collected. Into these channels I allowed the remainder of the molten ore to flow, and it extended itself through all these minor channels, and when it was cool I had several long bars of cast steel that, on my anvil, I could work up into any form.

After a few days, when my anvil was perfectly cool, I mounted it upon a block of wood and commenced to build a forge near by it, of brick and stone, into the fire-place of which I led a branch flexible tube of goat's skin from the fan-wheel, which I could easily detach and connect, and which gave me a blast instead of the usual bellows. At this forge I worked for a week steadily, turning out the simplest and most necessary tools, such as chisels, hammers, hatchets, axes, nails, bolts, plane irons, gouges, etc., which I tempered and hardened when needful. I also made myself tongs and shovels, pickaxe, and crowbars, and as fast as one tool was made at my forge, such as a pair of tongs and a hammer, I had means to make others better and rapidly. In this week I saw treasures gather up about me fast, and, having finished my iron work, I set to, to arrange them into tools. In the first place, by means of cold chisels, I cut out from a large mass of soft stone, that seemed as if it would suit my purpose, a grindstone some two feet in diameter; this I set up on two standards and connected with my water wheels. By means of this I could sharpen and bring into shape all the rough pieces of iron tools that I had forged out, and I had no difficulty in sharpening all my axes, planes, hatchets, chisels, etc., and, when necessary, giving them a finer edge on a whetstone, which I had found to suit my purpose. After getting these all in shape, my next task was to affix handles to them. This was not difficult to do, and it is hardly credible how soon I had my shop hung round about with useful tools. I soon had my planes in order, and my work then commenced to have a finish that it had before lacked. I did not stop here, however, for I was now in my element. I was ambitious of producing much better tools than I had yet finished by the very means that I already had, made to my hands, for creating them. I hope it is understood that the result of my smelting was not common iron, but what is known as Bessemer steel. By the numerous air passages through the ore and my fan-wheel, I had been enabled to turn out the result in steel in bulk by what is called the Bessemer process, leaving the metal all ready to my hand for tools, etc. This steel was not hard enough for some purposes for which I needed it, and having forged some pieces into the proper shape, I treated them to the crucible and blast, having beforehand stamped them with a cold chisel, and finally turned out some splendid files, which was what I most needed to advance in my iron work. As a boy, I used to be expert in this case-hardening of files and steel, and my knowledge now stood me in excellent need.

As soon as I got my files made, I felt as if I could make anything, and my next smelting procured for me—for it only took about twelve or fourteen hours to smelt—some thin sheets of steel, which I set to work upon to smooth by means of my grindstone, so as to make hand-saws; and, of a larger and thicker piece, two fine up-and-down sawmill saws, destined for my sawmill yet to be built. All of these I sharpened and hardened to the necessary temper, and by this time I discovered that my iron was of an excellent quality and as tough as possible. I had never seen finer, even in imported Swedish iron so much sought for at home. I think that the pleasantest noises I had yet heard since arriving on the island was my axe cutting into the side of a tree; my saw splitting the same into small boards when needed; and my planes smoothing these easily to a fine level surface. I did not attempt to saw out one board more than I needed, for I intended that my sawmill should do all that for me, and the planing too without much trouble on my part. So I set to work at this matter in earnest and cast me an axle for my water wheel, which I concluded to erect on my own side of the river. This wheel that I made was not much like the other, but was of wood and iron, strong and well built, and fastened with iron bolts, and set in iron sockets.

I dug away quite a space of the natural fall of Rapid River, and erected a strong flume and gateway, so as to control my wheel perfectly. I took little pains with the covering of my mill, making it hastily and with little care; but the foundations I laid out well and strong, and built it parallel with the side of the river, and had running down into the latter, from the mill, smooth timbers at an angle of about forty-five degrees, on which I intended, by means of my goats or the machinery of the mill itself, to "parbuckle" the logs up into the mill in front of the saw. For a mechanic the arranging of my mill was an easy task, not easy in its details, being laborious and hard, but easy I mean in its mechanical construction, which did not give me a moment's thought. About six weeks saw it all finished and everything in place; revolving knives for my planing-machine and a splendid up-and-down saw for my log-splitting. Of course all my machinery was of a different style, now that I had means to work with, than the rude wheels on the other side of the river. I had before me a good, substantial sawmill—rather rough, to be sure, in some details, but I did not care for that. Nobody, I am sorry to say, would ever look upon it and find fault with its want of finish.

Having this all done, I launched the "Fairy" above the falls and paddled up the river for about half a mile, marking on either bank with my axe the trees I wished to cut down—some of pine and cedar, and others of a hard, dark wood, like walnut, that I knew not the name of. A week's hard work with the axe saw some twenty of these in the water and floated to the dam, whence I rolled them out of the water as I needed them, and cut them into the requisite lengths for my sawmill, when I pushed them by handspikes again into the stream, and floated them in front of my inclined planes, up which they soon mounted by rolling themselves over and over in the two bights of a rope at each end, being slowly wound by the machinery of the mill on a drum inside, or, in other words, as sailors would say, "parbuckled" into the mill, where a few movements of the handspike put them in position on the cradle in front of the saw. Let it suffice for me to say that in a week or two I had all the planed boards that I should need for years, and also plank and joist nicely piled outside the mill, and covered with a light roof of rushes and cane from the rain and sun. It was a great thing for one man to be able to do so much, but then I had now got a start where nothing could stop me. Nature was under my thumb; I was the master.

All these works in iron, steel, and mill-building brought me to spring-like weather, in the month of October, and I began to see signs of returning summer. I hastened, therefore, to drop all these matters, and put myself and goats seriously to work to provide for my coming wants in the vegetable line, and for this purpose went to the landing-place and cleared a space of I should think an acre with a light subsoil plough and two yokes of goats, and planted the whole with different kinds of the seeds that I still had on hand, and which I had preserved. About this open space, or natural glade, were the usual trees and shrubs of the island, and with my axe I made them serve at distances for posts, filling in the intervals with limbs and shrubs, and, where absolutely necessary, using some of my precious boards, till I had made a very coarse, rough, but serviceable fence about my garden that goats or other animals could not get through and destroy the young vegetation when it should sprout up. It was here that I sowed some of my precious wheat, retaining a little in case of accident. In this garden I planted seeds that would mature late in the season, and would in a measure take care of themselves. Near the Hermitage I laid out a similar garden, with the same kind of fence, but not more than one hundred feet square. In this I planted all the little things that I needed at hand for my table, such as cucumbers, tomatoes, beans, radishes, celery, blackberries, strawberries, lettuce.

I found that my apple and pear seeds had taken root, for I visited them before winter had set in, and I took this opportunity, in ploughing, to manure with chopped fish the circular places that I had planted before the winter, and care to avoid turning up with the ploughshare any of the soil where these precious seeds were buried, and where the small, slight stems, leafless, now protruded. Spring came rapidly forward, and I found myself in almost warm weather and pleasant days before I had finished all my gardening, which was near the end of September.

These tasks nearly finished the year for me, within a month and a few days, and what had I accomplished? On Thursday, November 9, 1865, I was, by the providence of God, saved when all my shipmates were lost. I had been preserved for some good purpose evidently, or else the hand of the Almighty would have swept me out of existence with my messmates.

On that terrible day in November I was cast on shore, with scarcely any food, no hat, no coat, and without water. With no aid but that given me by God, and by the use of my own hands and brain, I was to-day sitting in front of my home, erected by myself alone. In this short space of time, one year, I had wrested from Nature many things, showing the supremacy of mind over matter, and knowledge, over ignorance and sloth. I had in this year made fire without the aid of matches, distilled salt water to procure fresh, made myself implements of defence, and erected towers of perpetual lamps, made myself flint, steel, and tinder, bows and arrows, fish-hooks and lines; discovered coal, sulphur, saltpetre, and iron, and captured goats, fish, seals, birds, etc., and at the end of the year found myself sitting at my house door surrounded with my flock of goats, my garden and farm planted, my mill and smelting-house in running order, my canoe at my feet in the quiet water of the cove, and everything about me that could please or charm the eye. From absolutely nothing I had created everything; that is to say, the ground was now so laid out that in the future I saw no end to the daring attempts that I should make, and could make with every chance of success. I felt, now that the year was ending, that my hardest work was done; that I had so much now to do with, that all that I should now undertake would be comparatively easy; but then, on the other hand, my ambition was so great that I could see things in the dim future that would tax the strength and brain of any man to consummate, but which from my temperament and loneliness I knew I should be forced to attempt. Many problems were already turning themselves over in my head, and from them I picked out this one, What is the position of your island in latitude and longitude?

I gave myself this as a special task, and whilst I was at work at little matters around about the Hermitage my mind kept asking me (for it had no one else to talk to), What is the position of your island in latitude and longitude? and it was repeated so often and so persistently that I tried to answer it, which I did in the following manner, as you shall hear.

CHAPTER XVII.

Make an astrolabe, and obtain the latitude of the island, and, by an eclipse of the moon, the longitude also. By means of the Epitome make a chart on Mercator's projection, and find out the distance from any known land.

I FOUND in my book a description of an instrument used by the ancients to ascertain altitudes and to measure angles, called an Astrolabe, which, upon careful study and examination of the cut, I felt confident would serve my purpose admirably. So to work I went, and in this manner. I made first a strong four-legged stool or bench, about three feet in height and four feet long, and two feet wide upon the top. I then took some nice planed pieces of my dark hardwood and made a smooth surface about an inch thick and five feet square. On this, afterwards to be erected on the stool at right angles like an inverted letter T, I drew a circle with a pair of immense dividers that I made for this purpose, taking in all the area possible, which made my circle about fifty-nine inches in diameter, leaving a margin of one inch,—supposing my inches to have been of the right length; and this I determined by the length of the knuckle of my thumb, which I formerly used for quick measurement, and from which standard I constructed the only rule I ever have used on the island. How nearly correct it is I have no means of knowing. This groove I impressed into the wood by repeatedly turning the dividers around the circumference. I then went to work and subdivided this circle into degrees and minutes, which I did by marking the circle once across at any angle passing through the centre mark, and then by another mark crossing this one at exactly right angles, which I determined by means of my dividers—as laid down in Bowditch's Epitome—by the use of them at equal distances from the centre on the line already marked, sweeping them till the two lines crossed beyond the circumference, making a small mark there so as to erect a perpendicular on the base already drawn. This cut my circle at once into quadrants of 90° each, and these were subdivided again in like manner. I made the circle large on purpose, so as to be able to mark it plainly to sections of one minute each, and by its size to avoid any error in any angle, the chances of which were greatly decreased by every inch of diameter. As I constructed it, I had nearly one-half an inch of circumference to mark sixty minutes upon, and as I only subdivided one of the quadrants it did not take me very long, each degree being represented by a space slightly smaller than a half inch, which was a good large scale to work upon. Having finished the marking of my board I nailed it firmly to the stool in an upright position, with the quadrant, that I had carefully subdivided on the marked circumference, pointing with one of its angles to zenith, and the other on a line with the top of the stool. I then procured a nice straight piece of cane some six feet in length and about an inch in diameter, and with a heated rod of iron burned out all the pith between each joint till I had made a nice tube of that length. Just within the aperture at one end I fastened with a little fish glue a large strong hair from the beard of one of my goats. I then fastened, by means of a hole through the centre of my upright disc, this tube or telescope to it on the side that was subdivided into degrees, and about an inch from the face. I fastened this so that it was held firmly in place, and yet could be moved upon its centre by the pressure of my hand on either arm. This tube I then furnished with a small delicate pin on the outside, in an exact line with the stretched hair inside the tube, and pointing to the degrees and minutes on the marked circumference on the disc, which it almost touched. In other words, if I moved one arm of the tube, the needle on the outside would follow the grooved circumference on the disc, and upon being released would mark some given degree or minute. Having gotten this machine all in order and complete, I placed it one day so as to examine the sun near noon, and here is how I obtained my latitude. What I was doing now was not so very difficult. I well knew that there were several ways to determine latitude. I was aware that the difference of a minute or two even in my altitude, as apparently observed, would not disturb my computation more than a mile or so. In fact each minute marked upon the disc practically stood for one mile of latitude, and the mean of several observations would correct even any errors from this cause.

I waited till I knew that it was nearly noon by the appearance of the sun, and then commenced operations. In the first place I aimed my tube at the sun, and to be able to do so without injuring my eye, I would say that I had fitted the orifice of the tube nearest to me with a piece of smoke-colored membrane or backbone of the squid, which is as transparent as glass, and very thin and delicate. Having, by moving the tube with my hand, brought the sun so that it seemed to stand upon the hair in the outer end of the tube, or like a great capital O upon a base line O, I left it carefully in that position for a moment or two, and then applied my eye again, and found, as I supposed, that the sun no longer seemingly rested upon the hair in my tube, but had risen, which forced me to again lower the arm nearest me and elevate the other extremity, and proved to me that it was not yet noon, and that the sun had not yet reached the meridian. This I did many times, till at last the sun seemed for a minute or so to stand still, as sailors say, and I knew that it was at meridian. I took good care not to touch the instrument, but waited quietly till, by glancing through it, I saw in a few moments the disc of the sun, or lower limb as it is termed, begin to drop below the hair in my tube, and I was then positive that it had passed the meridian. Being assured of this, I went carefully to the marked circumference on the upright disc and noted carefully the degree and minute to which the needle in the side of the tube pointed, which in this case was 54° 51'. Having carefully marked this down with ink upon birch bark, I went again to the other end of the tube, and, elevating it, brought the outer end down toward the sea till the hair and the horizon seemed to be one. I then again carefully observed the degree and minute at which the needle pointed, which in this case was 7° 16', and my task was done; for, by subtracting 7° 16' from 54° 51' I obtained 47° 35', which was exactly the apparent altitude of the sun at noon on September 22, 1866, civil account; and, having that, it was easy to determine the latitude in the following manner:—

At noon observe the altitude of the sun's lower limb bearing North	47° 35'
Add for semi-diameter, dip, etc.	12'
	47° 47'
Subtract from	90° 00'
Sun's zenith distance	42° 13' S.
Declination for longitude, say 115° W	8' S.
Latitude by observation	42° 21' S.

Thus I demonstrated the latitude of my island; but now for the longitude. To obtain that I knew that I must first ascertain the time at the island: I could do nothing without that; for longitude was, as I well knew, simply time changed into degrees. I thought of fifty different ways to obtain correct time, but believed none of them sufficiently accurate for my purpose. I could make a sundial for one thing, find out the length of the day by the Epitome and Nautical Almanac, make candles to burn such a length of time, sand to run down an inclined plane at such a rate, but none of these would do.

The difference of a minute, or one-sixtieth of a degree, in an observed altitude would only affect, as I have said, my latitude just one mile, whilst an error of time of one minute from true time would, as I was well aware, throw my longitude out just fifteen miles; hence it behoved me to have exact time if I desired to get exact longitude, and therefore I saw nothing for it but that I must construct a clock, and at it I went. It was not such an enormous undertaking after all. Of course I should make it of wood, and in my boyhood I knew many wooden clocks that kept excellent time; besides, if I could only construct something that would keep time for an hour or two without much error, it would answer my purpose. If I had a clock that I could set at noon by my observation, nearly correct, I could correct it perfectly by an afternoon observation, and have for an hour or so true time, even if it did gain or lose a few minutes in twenty-four hours. So to work I set, and soon turned out the few small wheels necessary, and the weight and pendulum for the same. I spent little time upon the non-essentials, but put it together inside my house on the wall, open so that I could get at it, and furnished it with wooden hands and a thin wooden face.

After I had arranged it and found that it would tick, and by observations at noon for a few days been able to regulate the pendulum, I went diving into the Epitome and the Nautical Almanac as to how I should utilize it so as to get my longitude, after all; when one evening, in turning over the Nautical

Almanac, which was calculated for 1866, 1867, 1868, and 1869, my eye fell upon the following, and I felt that my task was done:—

Total eclipse of the moon, September 30,1866, invisible at Greenwich, visible in South America, South Pacific Ocean, and parts of Africa, Asia, and Indian Ocean.

FORMULA (CIVIL ACCOUNT).

	Day.	Hour.	Min.	
Moon enters penumbra	30	5	44	A.M.
Moon enters shadow	30	6	53	"
Total phase begins	30	8	49	"
Total phase ends	30	9	39	"
Moon leaves shadow	30	10	45	"
Moon leaves penumbra	30	11	55	"

This was all I needed to verify my longitude past peradventure, and I went to work at once, calculating when the eclipse ought to take place, nearly, with me.

At a rough calculation I knew that my island was situated somewhere between the 110° and 120° of longitude west of Greenwich, that is to say, in the neighborhood of seven hours' difference of time later than Greenwich time. Therefore I knew that if the moon entered the penumbra at Greenwich (although invisible) on the 30d. 5h. 44 min. A.M. that I ought to look for it to occur visibly to my eyes somewhere from one to two o'clock in the afternoon of the same day, or seven hours later. The *exact* difference in the time between Greenwich and that to be observed on my island, changed into degrees and minutes, would, of course be the true longitude west of Greenwich.

It was with the utmost anxiety that I awaited the coming of the 30th of September, for it all depended upon pleasant weather whether or not I should be able to make my observation. I placed my astrolabe so as to be able to move it quickly in any needed direction, as I intended to use the tube to look at the sun through so as not to blind my eyes. I also prepared my birch bark in the house, and commenced practising myself in counting seconds, for I should have to leave my instrument and go to the house, counting all the time to note the time marked by my clock. I found upon practice that I could not make this work very successfully, and that according to the state of my feelings or excitement I counted long and short minutes. This would not do; I must invent something better; and I finally bethought myself of counting the beatings of my pulse with the finger of one hand upon the wrist of the other, and applying the proportion to the interval between the observed time by my clock.

The morning at last came that I so much desired, and nothing could be more beautiful than the balmy, spring-like day that surrounded me. The sky was cloudless and the sun shone down in splendor through a clear and pure atmosphere. The morning passed slowly away, and it seemed as if the moon and sun would never approach each other; but finally, in the afternoon, the heavens showed me that the eclipse would soon take place, and I made my arrangements to take four observations, as follows: Time when moon entered shadow; time when total phase began; time when total phase ended; time when moon left shadow.

Nothing could have been better than the afternoon I experienced to make these observations, and in less than six hours the whole affair was over, with the following result, I having carefully regulated my clock as near as possible by an observation at noon:—

	Day.	Hour.	Min.
Moon enters shadow at island (civil account)	30	2	50 P.M.
Moon enters shadow at Greenwich	30	6	53 A.M.
Difference		7	57
Total phase begins at island	30	4	48 P.M.
Total phase begins at Greenwich	30	8	49 A.M.
Difference		7	59
Total phase ends at island	30	5	34 P.M.
Total phase ends at Greenwich	30	9	39 A.M.
Difference		7	55
Moon leaves shadow at island	30	6	41 P.M.
Moon leaves shadow at Greenwich	30	10	45 A.M.
Difference		7	56

	Hours.	Min.
Sum of differences, four observations	31	47

	Hours.	Min.	Sec.
Mean of same	7	56	45

Which, reduced to time, gives the longitude of the island 119° 11′ 15″ west of Greenwich.

There, my problem was done and I was for the moment happy. Perhaps some will wonder why I cared to obtain the latitude and longitude of my island at all. Let me explain. My Bowditch's Epitome gave the latitude and longitude of all prominent capes, harbors, headlands, light-houses, etc., in the whole Pacific Ocean. In other words, knowing now the latitude and longitude of my own island, I had only to project a chart on Mercator's projection, pricking off the relative positions of the land on all sides of me, as well as the position of my island, to have a practical and useful chart. Of course I should not be able to draw the coast line or the circumference of any island, but my chart would show just what latitude and longitude Easter Island was in, for instance, and just how far and in exactly what direction my island lay from it. Also, how far I was from the American coast, and the exact distance and course from any of the principal ports such as Lima, Valparaiso, Pisco, etc. How far from New Zealand and the Society Islands, and in what direction from them.

Having marked the exact latitude and longitude of each of these places, which were fully given in the Epitome, on my chart, I could call upon my memory often to fill in the coast lines, and even if I should in the case of the islands, make them even imaginary, there would be no harm done, for the little black star on each would show me where the latitude and longitude met exactly, and I should be furnished with a practical chart as far as sea navigation was concerned, but not one that would be of much account in entering any harbors.

I cannot say that at this time I had any fixed plan of escaping from the island, but I very well knew that nothing in the world would aid me so much in the attempt as to know the position in latitude and longitude that the island occupied, and a chart of the surrounding seas, with its numerous islands and headlands on the main land. It can well be conceived that my first task after determining the position of my island was to turn to the Epitome to ascertain the nearest land to me there marked down, and after diligent search this is what I found:—

"Easter Island Peak," 27° 8' south latitude and 109° 17' west longitude.

"Island," 28° 6' south latitude and 95° 12' west longitude.

"Group of Islands," 31° 3' south latitude and 129° 24' west longitude.

"Massafuera," 33° 45' south latitude and 80° 47' west longitude, which I speedily worked out, by the principles of Mercator's sailing, to be in course and distance from my island, as follows:—

	Course.	Distance.
Easter Island Peak	N. N. E. ½ E.	1,040 miles.
Island	N. E. ¾ E.	1,440 ”
Group of Islands	N. W. ¾ N.	840 ”
Massafuera	N. N. E. ¼ E.	1,540 ”

Of these four places only two ever had a name, and I did not know whether Easter Island was inhabited or not, and about Massafuera I was totally ignorant.

Easter Island, I knew, of course, was one of the so-called Society Islands, and was the nearest practical land to which I could escape. But how was I safely to pass over a thousand miles of water? This investigation only proved to me what I had so long feared, namely, that my island was out of the track of all trade, and that it would be a miracle should I be preserved by the arrival of any vessel. I knew now that I must really give up all hope in that direction, and set to work seriously to help myself.

I therefore applied myself with great vigor to my chart which I outlined upon nice goatskin parchment, which I glued together till I had a surface nearly four feet square, upon which I could lay out all the Pacific Ocean on a nice, large scale, by Mercator's projection. I went on with my daily work, and made this matter one for evening amusement, and as I pricked off the latitude and longitude of some well-known place, that I in former years had visited, my heart swelled within me with grief and mortification, and I had often to stop and wipe the tears from my eyes before I could proceed.

Release from my prison seemed farther from me than ever, as I advanced in my task, and although I had a sort of morbid pleasure in my work, and a fascination to linger over it, yet I saw plainly that I was indeed cast away; for what could I do alone in a boat, even supposing that I could build one strong enough to resist one thousand miles of water? Who was to steer when I was asleep? and then supposing I should be able to arrive at Easter Island, what guarantee had I that I should not be murdered at once by the natives?

No, here I was fixed beyond fate upon my own island, where, with the exception of companionship, I had everything that human heart could wish for. But on the other hand, without companionship I lacked everything that is worth living for in this world. I felt that the problem of all problems hereafter to me would be how can I escape to some civilized country in safety? And from what I now knew, it seemed as if it would remain a problem till my bones were left whitening in the Hermitage.

My discovery of the latitude and longitude of the island had brought me no comfort, and I felt much more uneasy now than I did before finishing my task. But as the summer weather came on, I regained to a degree my good spirits, keeping, however, the problem of escape continually working in my mind, for I knew that there must be some way to solve it, especially with the resources that I had gathered around about me.

CHAPTER XVIII.

A resumé of three years on the island. Daily routine of life. Inventions, discoveries, etc. Fortification of the Hermitage. Manufacture of cannon and guns. Perfection and improvement of the machine shop. Implicit faith of ultimately overcoming all obstacles and escaping from the island. Desire to accumulate some kind of portable wealth to carry with me, and decide to explore the island for its hidden wealth and the surrounding ocean for pearl oysters.

I SHALL not become tedious by inflicting upon my readers the routine of each day, or even of each month or year that I have passed on this island, but shall pick out the most startling events of my life here, both as to the inventions that I have made and the accidents and adventures of which I have been the victim and hero.

Of course my discovery of iron gave me wonderful power to advance and preserve myself. After my first set of tools were made, as I have enumerated in detail, all other work, even if slow, was comparatively easy.

My next task, after making the common tools that I needed and various castings that were useful to me, was to erect a turning lathe,—one for wood, which was quite simple, and one for iron, which was a work of some magnitude,—and a whole year elapsed before I had it perfected to my taste. The castings were rough, but solid and useful, and the other parts were, with care and attention, at last made mathematically true, and this, with a drilling machine and some iron rollers to roll out my metal when coming from the furnace, completed my iron foundry, as I was now pleased to call it.

Having all these things about me it was a small matter to cast several small cannon, of some four or six pound calibre, and bore them out on my turning-lathe and table. These I mounted on wooden trucks, and placed one on East Signal Point, one on Eastern Cape, one on South Cape, which I transported there by water in the canoe Fairy, one on Penguin Point, and one on West Signal Point. It was fun for me to make these things, and therefore, to protect myself still more, I made a number, of smaller calibre even, which I placed pointing out through embrasures in a wall with which I had encircled the Hermitage, and surrounded with a strong picket fence, made of cast-iron, which I found no difficulty in casting in sections of nearly ten feet in length. At all the stations at the extremities of the island I hid a little amount of ammunition, near the cannon erected, and also a flint and steel and a limestock or slow-match, so that at any time, if needful, I could load one of these cannon at once and discharge it. The touchholes I covered nicely with a piece of goatskin, so as to protect the guns from the weather, and fitted all the muzzles with a wooden plug, so that the interior would be kept clear and dry.

PLACING THE CANNON.—Page 190.

In the wall that now surrounded my Hermitage I built a strong iron gate, that I could see through and yet too strong to be broken down by any savage hands. The iron fence or comb which ran round the summit of this wall, and of which I have spoken, crossed also above the gateway, and made my house impregnable to anything except artillery. My doorway facing this, in the Hermitage itself, had long been replaced by a nice hard-wood one, with iron hinges, with several loopholes left, through which I could poke a gun-barrel or discharge an arrow.

I had six cannon mounted on my wall, two in front, two on each side, and one in rear, which was, however, naturally protected by a thick and almost impenetrable grove of trees and undergrowth. These guns were mounted in a peculiar manner upon carriages that allowed the muzzles to be depressed at least thirty degrees, and I kept in store, to load them with, quantities of iron ball castings, from the size of an English walnut to a common musket bullet, which at close quarters would do fearful execution. I approached these guns, from the interior, by means of step ladders, made of wood, leading up to each from the enclosure, and an oval hole, like an inverted letter U, was left in the iron fencing to allow the muzzle to protrude over the wall. This opening, however, was small, and not large enough to admit even the head of a man, much less his body. The erection of the whole wall, which was some nine feet high, cost me infinite labor and patience.

The fencing on top of it was, as I have said, rapidly turned out from the casting mould, and gave me, comparatively speaking, little trouble. To further protect this my fortress from any assaults, I brought the water underground from Rapid River into the Hermitage, through a series of pipes made of pottery thoroughly baked, glazed, and made so as to fit one into the other, and controlled the flow by means of a stopcock fixed into a piece of cane. The signs of this underground connection with Rapid River I took care to thoroughly efface. And, furthermore, I made it a duty to always keep at least six months' salted provisions in store, ahead of all demands,—such as salted and smoked herring, salmon, and other fish, with corned and dried goat's flesh, and some few preserved vegetables such as I might have on hand.

In rear of my house, between the end of the house and the wall, I dug a subterranean passage, leading under my wall, and coming again to the surface in the midst of a seemingly impenetrable thicket of undergrowth, some thirty yards away from the wall. This outlet was carefully closed by a trapdoor, and soil even strewed on top and grass allowed to grow over it. I did not know but what there might come a time when I should have to use this passage, as the last recourse, to save my life; and although now in security I built it carefully, to be prepared for what might happen in the future.

After all these tasks for my defence were finished I commenced upon a set of guns and pistols, or rather rifles,—for I had not the slightest use for a shotgun, being able, in a hundred ways, by means of steel-traps and similar devices, to capture all the birds and animals I needed,—which I desired to protect myself against any human enemies, should such ever appear. To this end I easily bored myself out some four nice rifle barrels, and some half dozen of a smaller size for pistols; these I had to stock, and mount with the old-fashioned flint and steel, for I had no means of making any percussion-powder. I worked at these for a long time, but at last I had them all in good order, and used to amuse myself by practising with ball at the pigeons on the trees, and the ducks on the river. I did not make the best shooting in the world, for, not being able to procure lead, I was forced to make my bullets of steel, and to revolve them in a cylinder for a long time with sand, to make them globular and regular. The barrels of my guns and pistols also had to be smooth bored to use these projectiles; as a rifled barrel, if I could have made one, would have been ruined by cast-steel bullets; still at a hundred yards, with a nice greased patch, I was able to make good execution, and the pistols shot with strength at a distance of at least twenty yards. Both weapons suited me practically, and with my guns I had no difficulty in shooting several of the wild goats, and also seals, whenever I needed their meat or skins.

My flock of tame goats all this while had grown and increased, and I added to my home comforts cheese and butter; but I made the wheel on the further side of the river do all the churning by a simple application of the machinery to a revolving clapper in an upright churn.

The parchment windows in the Hermitage had long since been reinforced by iron shutters on the outside, that, if needed, could be bolted securely on the inside, and the roof had been refitted and made of timber and boards, and the whole covered with tiles, so as to be fireproof. Up through this roof I had also built a tower, of brick, not very large but quite high, some feet above the ridge-pole, which I mounted to by a flight of stairs from the attic; for the upper part of the house was floored off and completed when I erected the new roof, having no want now of either boards or timber.

Up to this tower I trotted every morning before unbarring the door of the Hermitage or the gate of the enclosure. From this lookout I could see quite well in several directions, and notice if anything had been touched or changed from the evening before. I missed, I think, at this time, books more than anything, but then, again, from the very want of them, I was forced to study with my Epitome and Book of Useful Arts and Sciences, which possibly I might have thrown to one side for less useful but more entertaining ones if I had had them. Wanting them, I was becoming versed in many things which when I came upon the island I knew nothing about, and I was pleased to think that, although alone, I was improving, and the usefulness of a really good book was brought forcibly before me each day, for I could not open either of mine without finding food for reflection and study. I had always had my head full of vagaries of different kinds that I should like some time to try and experiment upon, and here seemed my opportunity; and it will be observed, in its proper place, further on, that I attempted many things.

It was, I think, in my third year that I felt that my daily routine was fixed for life, as far as concerned comforts and food; for by that time I had wheat for my bread, and all kinds of vegetables and fruits that I have before enumerated, in profusion. My apple and pear trees would soon begin to bear, and in a year or two more I should have them to add to my comforts. I had already commenced to preserve blackberries, strawberries, etc., and found that my maple trees, in the spring, were just as prolific as those in my Vermont home, and that I had no difficulty in obtaining all the sugar I needed. Roasted wheat had, however, to stand me instead of Java coffee, but this made me quite a pleasant drink.

All these comforts were enhanced by a climate so uniform in temperature that it was a pleasure to even exist, the winters bringing scarcely an inch of snow or ice with them, and the summers even and mild; warm, to be sure, but still far from being hot or oppressive. As I have said so often in this narrative before, what in the world could one want in excess of all this but companionship? Ah! it is little known how many bitter hours of solitude I passed in gathering all these comforts about me, and how, with a tenderness almost womanly, I made friends with every kid, duck, young bird, seal, and living animal that I gathered around me, and made pets of them all. My hardest duties were to destroy these animals for my own consumption, and I latterly destroyed what I could with the gun rather than touch one of those that were domesticated. Some of these I could not bear to lay my hand upon, especially my young kids and team of goats; but thank God there was no need of it. I could easily destroy one of their species, when I needed the flesh, with my rifle, for I veritably believe that I should have gone without animal food rather than touch one of these pets. Two of the kids, especially, followed me about all the time, and even into my canoe when I took short trips abroad.

I had by this time, by means of snares, captured seven species of birds which resembled our blackbirds and bobolinks of the north, and I took great delight in feeding them in the cages I had made for them, and listening to their music in the morning and evening hours. Long search had taught me to feel sure that the island had no venomous insects or reptiles, and it was also wholly free from that nuisance the horse-fly, which is said to follow civilization, and that other pest, the mosquito, was wholly unknown. In their stead there were a few sand-fleas, a sort of wood-tick, which troubled the goats somewhat, and a small black wood-fly, that was not troublesome except in some seasons, in the woods, and on the coast. In December and January, green-headed flies were apt to take hold of me once in a while, but not so as to incommode me.

The air was so pure that meat would keep a long while without putrefaction, even in the warm weather, and having nothing better to do to take up my mind, I had, during the past winter, collected quite an amount of thin ice from Rapid River, which, in a small subterranean ice-house, roofed over with planks, and covered with sawdust, I had stored for summer use, and on very warm days luxuriated in.

This life of solitude had made me tender to even inanimate things, and it was wonderful to myself how the passion, self-importance, and arbitrary manner of one accustomed to command at sea was dying out in me. I began to almost have a reverence for flowers and all beautiful inanimate things, and many hours of my life were passed in my garden and on my farm, but especially the former, in examining and cultivating some beautiful wild flower or trailing vine that I had transported hence from the forest. I felt even that the bearing of my body was changed from what it used to be when in days gone by I trod the quarter-deck in all the pride and majesty of power.

I cannot say that I was at this time contented, but I can say that I was much more patient, and the impetuosity of my temperament was greatly subdued, and many things, both animate and inanimate, were becoming, in spite of myself, very dear to my eyes. I even at times began to feel homesick when I was absent over a day, in my canoe, from the Hermitage, and came back to its comforts with an exclamation of gratification and a swelling of the heart with joy when it came in view, and showed itself intact during my temporary absence; and the welcome given me by my goats, tame pigeons, ducks, and birds was very touching, and, as I have said, endeared them to me greatly. Still for no moment did the problem of escape leave my mind. Although without relatives or children, I often dreamed of escaping from the island and returning with friends to enjoy it with me and end my days here in peace. I often thought how happy I could be here, far from the cares of the world and all its vain excitements, could I see around about me smiling faces of my fellow-men, who would look up to me as their benefactor and ruler, for I had yet left some of the seaman's instinct of desire to rule.

Up to this time I had done little exploring of the island; my first trip around about it had been my last, and my excursions into the interior had been short, and without making any material discovery of moment. This was caused by the great tasks that I had given myself near home, and the consummation of which had taken all my time. I had worked very hard to accomplish all that was laid out before my eyes, and had had little time for wandering about or being idle.

No sign of any vessel, or canoes of savages, had ever disturbed me. I had often, during the last year, visited the points of my island nearest to me, *i.e.* East and West Signal Points and the breakwater, but no welcome sail had ever met my eye. The sight of the ocean also from these points always gave me the blues, and sent me home troubled and discontented, for the intellect given me by the Creator on such occasions rebelled against my fate, and the ocean seemed my enemy, whom I must overcome, and whom I could overcome if I could only think of the means, for I would never acknowledge myself beaten, but only unable for the present to cope with my adversary; and I used to talk to it, and say: "Some day, thou mighty sea, with God's help, I will overcome and conquer thee, and compel thee to carry me wherever I desire to be borne. Power has been given man over the beasts of the field and over all nature, and I have only to use my mind, with which God has endowed me, to some day make thee, now my master, my slave. Roll on, therefore, for a day shall come, God willing, in which thy billows shall carry me, and the winds of heaven waft me to civilized lands, where the Creator of both thee and me is adored and worshipped. You shall not always separate me from the place whence I came. With my strong hold that I have obtained I will yet overcome thee, and make thee my steed of deliverance, instead of, as now, the boundary line of my imprisonment."

My daily life at about this time was something like this. I arose in the morning, and, if the season would admit of it, took a plunge in Stillwater Cove, first, however, visiting my tower to see if everything was all right in all directions. I usually, with a sailor's habits, arose early, and with the sun. After my bath I proceeded to feed my numerous flock of goats, kids, pigeons, etc., and then to the cares of my dairy, milking my goats and conveying the result of my labors to my ice-house, near by, to be kept there, and at proper season to be made into butter and cheese. Then to my breakfast, which I could change in many various ways, as my appetite dictated, always commencing the same, in these days, by thanking God for his preservation of me, and expressing gratitude for the food before me, and hopefulness of ultimate delivery from my island prison. After breakfast I went about any work that might be on hand, such as fishing, gunning, or arranging my household things, working in my iron ore, conveying coal or iron from the mines, or running my sawmill, or else digging in my garden or attending to my farm near the landing-place, and the thousand and one daily things that had to be done with one pair of hands, to keep my establishment in order.

When I thought it noon by the sun (for I soon gave over the attempt to keep my clumsy clock agoing after I had obtained my latitude and longitude) I repaired to the Hermitage, and if the weather was warm and pleasant made my meal in the outer air, under the shade of a fine large tree of the maple species, surrounded by my domestic birds; if in winter, by my fireside, inside the house. After dinner I again commenced my daily toil, first taking a good long smoke of my favorite pipe, which, all things considered, was my greatest solace, and after this taking up the work that I had laid down at the dinner hour. I kept myself employed till sunset, or nearly so,—for I did not now overwork myself as I used to in the beginning, in my impetuosity, but took everything mildly, quietly, and comfortably,—when I again called my flock together and attended to my milking. I knew that cheeses would keep a long while, and, looking always forward to an escape, I was gradually laying up a stock of this nutritious article for use in the future should I ever need it, knowing well how palatable and refreshing it always is at sea. After the milking was finished, which was not till I had gathered the flock from their feeding pastures, I entered my house for the night, taking with me one or two of my favorite kids, and barring the iron gate in the enclosure wall carefully behind me, and doing the same with the door of the Hermitage.

Once within, I lighted my lamps and gave myself plenty of light, and took my supper, followed by the inevitable pipe, and often a glass of my claret wine, as I called it, made from the pure juice of the grape. Then I got out a sheet of parchment and commenced a history of the day's proceedings, which I wrote down in detail, and from which this narrative is condensed. This was a very important task, for upon the daily performance of it rested the accuracy of my calendar. This often carried me well into the evening, and if it did not, and I was not very tired, I got out my Bowditch's Epitome and solved a problem or two, and then turned to my Book of Useful Arts and Sciences and stored my mind with some new fact, or tried to decipher some of the things that were daily becoming more clear to me, and which I had commenced by understanding scarcely a word about. When I found myself nodding over this work I quietly betook myself to bed, preferring, as a rule, my upright bedstead to the swinging hammock. I never put out the lights and only removed my outer clothing when I slept, but then the latter was a very natural act to a person who had for years turned in "all a standing," as sailors say, and ready for a call at any time of the night or day. My arms and ammunition were placed within easy access of my hands, and, commending my soul to God, I used to sleep.

In winter I kept of course more within doors, and busied myself upon my clothing and such things as needed sewing and lashing together, fixing little nicknacks of shell and wood around about the room, to hold flowers and ferns, or any little thing that had attracted my eye, or would please me in my solitude. On rainy days I almost always went to work in my smelting house at the forge, and if there was nothing else to do I would busy myself in the making of nails for future use, I having to beat out each one on the anvil; but when finished each of my nails was a wrought one, and worth a dozen cast by machinery. I always found plenty to do here, but I worked leisurely, always looking toward the future. I got together a large quantity of rolled iron, of about a quarter of an inch in thickness, and in sheets nearly two feet wide and some eight or nine in length. This workshop I kept improving till I had, besides my forge and all its tools, turning-lathes both for wood and iron, many other useful things, which I had constructed at odd times, such as a small but very strong derrick, which I fitted with iron blocks and chains and with a winch and band, so that I was able to handle large masses of iron with ease. My rollers, also, for rolling out the iron when at a white heat, were in this room, and I had long since improved and strengthened my water-wheel, so that I had all the power at any time that I needed or desired, to move any or all of my machinery.

Besides gathering together these sheets of iron I put them under my drilling machine and punched the edges with holes of an uniform size, so that they could at some time be riveted together, for I had an idea in my head what I should use them for. The making of a large number of rivets to fit these holes also took plenty of my time, as did the making of different sizes of spikes, and once in a while some new tool that I felt the need of. My files, also, once in a while had to be re-marked and again hardened, and thus I found myself always with plenty to do whenever I entered the smelting-house; and it was there that I enjoyed myself the most, for I was a born mechanic, and I liked the work, and nothing pleased me so much as to see something turning out under my hand from a crude mass of iron into some useful tool, or article of which I had need. Therefore when the stormy and rainy days came it was with absolute pleasure that I walked into my smelting-house and set to work. It was here that I saw my deliverance must be worked out, and never a day passed but what my machinery was improved or increased in some way, and made more perfect and reliable. A great deal of it, to be sure, was crude, but it was also practical; and when a piece of machinery would not perform well I went to work, and kept at it until it would, and in the end had not the slightest trouble in rolling, casting, drilling, planing, and turning iron or cast-steel, in all reasonable shapes. To be sure my machinery was not painted, or even well finished, except in the working parts, but to those sections I gave a mechanic's care. I not only worked here, however, on stormy days alone, but also nearly every spare moment that I had from other duties that were also pressing.

As my riches began to accumulate I began to think seriously of exploring the island for its hidden wealth, and see if I could not during these years that I was waiting for escape—which I had made up my mind was sure to come— lay up enough wealth, in some shape, to take with me when I should depart, that would make me rich for the remainder of my days. Knowing that such wealth, to be conveyed away by me, must necessarily be in a small compass, I was working out a problem at this very time to explore the bottom of the ocean around my island, and see if I could not hit upon some pearl-oyster beds, whence I could draw riches to carry away with me when I should leave this island, and the theory that I had gotten into my head, and which I was trying to put into actual practice, was the following:—

CHAPTER XIX.

Construct a submarine boat, to be propelled by goat power and to make its own air, to examine the bottom of the ocean near the island for pearl-oysters.

YES, as I have hinted in the preceding chapter, I had fully made up my mind to explore the *bottom* of the ocean that surrounded my island, and I did not intend to commence in the stupid way in which the former Crusoe went to work, and build me a boat and then be unable to launch it. Far from it. My very first care was to erect ways running down into Stillwater Cove, made out of large square timbers, placed at a considerable decline, so that I felt confident that what I should erect upon them could be launched by me into the water without difficulty or trouble. These ways I bolted strongly together, and made firm and enduring, and upon them erected a kind of raft, which I kept in place by means of upright iron bolts through the timbers of the ways, which prevented it, for the time being, from slipping into the water if it should be so inclined, but which, when the bolts were removed, and the three timbers upon which it rested well greased, I felt sure would, at the proper moment desired, slip into Stillwater Cove.

Upon this raft I commenced to construct my submarine boat. These launching-ways were erected near the smelting house, and not far below the falls, just where the water became deep enough for my purpose, and yet as near as possible of access to my forge and shop. The raft that I built and erected upon the ways was only as a cradle to support my submarine boat so that I could float the whole affair to the mouth of Stillwater Cove before allowing the latter to be submerged; for where I now was there was not water enough for my experiment, and I well knew that if my boat, which was to be of iron, was once launched, and should, by its displacement or specific gravity, go to the bottom, that I should be unable to raise it again, and that in the water directly in front of the ways it would touch the bottom even before it would be submerged. On the other hand, if I should erect my ways running into deep water at some place near the mouth of Stillwater Cove, and opposite Point Deliverance, I should have no means at hand to complete it, all my forges, iron-work, tools, and shop being too far distant for such an undertaking. I saw, therefore, that I must construct it near to my foundry, and hence I chose this method of a cradle, or raft, to carry out my plan. This raft, or cradle as I shall call it in future, was of itself quite an undertaking, for I had to make it of mortised pieces of wood, so that at the proper time I could take it to pieces, and allow its load, the submarine boat, to drop into the ocean, at some place yet to be determined, to which I should tow it, where the water would be smooth, and protected from the billows of the ocean, and not too deep for my experiment.

I had also another care in forming this cradle, and that was, that it should be buoyant enough to sustain the submarine boat, and not, when launched, go to the bottom of Stillwater Cove with its precious freight, on account of the weight of the latter. This cradle, therefore, took both time and care to make, and long hours were passed by me in figuring out the weight of the iron boat I was about to build, and how large and extensive my cradle ought to be to sustain it. By studying my book, and by experimenting in different ways with small vessels of pottery and bladders blown up with air, that I submerged, I got at what I thought would be about the weight of my submarine boat and its relation to the cradle, and I saw plainly that the latter would have to be improved in some way to sustain the necessary weight. So this is how I went to work to overcome this obstacle.

On the two long sides of the cradle running parallel to the timber ways, beyond which they extended several feet (although the ways themselves were some six feet wide from the outside of one timber to the outside of the other, by my island rule), I lashed firmly with iron bands and bolts two water-tight iron tanks, which I constructed of my rolled iron, riveted together, fully six feet long, three feet wide, and three feet deep. The dimensions of the cradle itself were about these: Ten feet wide and eighteen feet in length, resting firmly upon the three declined timbers or ways, which were six feet wide from side to side and some forty feet in length from where they commenced on the shore to their terminus under the water in Stillwater Cove, at a depth of about eight or nine feet at high water. They were kept in place by their own weight, being of as large a size as I could handle with my team of goats, and of hard-wood, the inclination they received from the shore ends forcing the outer ends to the bottom of the water. Of course these ways were not made of one piece of timber but of several, which were as large as I dared cut them with any hope of being able to handle them, and were fished together to make the required length, being first sawed out at the mill, planed upon the upper side by hand, and then let down again over the inclined planes of the mill into Rapid River, and thence thrust over the falls into the shallow water and conveyed to their place, where I pulled them on shore by means of rollers and my team of goats, till I had each in place and mounted upon short uprights of other timber, that I had placed at equal distances from each other, and higher one than the other as they were erected landward from the water.

The underpinning of my cradle was exactly like the wooden underpinning of a house, and consisted of a parallelogram, eighteen feet by ten feet, with timbers of about eight inches square. Across these timbers were placed smaller ones in sockets, exactly as slats are placed across a bed, and this was to form the foundations upon which I was to erect my boat.

When I desired to submerge it I had only to saw away each of these slats, on either side, and it would drop into the ocean, leaving the outer framework—or bedstead, if you please—floating; for my boat was to be built, of course, less than eighteen feet long and ten wide, so as to rest wholly upon these slats and not upon the framework of the cradle that supported the slats. This took me a long time to finish; but what was time to me whilst revolving the problem of my escape, which was not yet solved. Till I knew *how* I was to escape I should never again be in a hurry.

To build my boat I commenced by making two watertight tanks, each sixteen feet long and two feet square, and two smaller ones, each six feet long and of the same dimensions otherwise as the long ones; these, placed upon the slats of my cradle, gave me a parallelogram composed of four water-tight tanks, all made out of my rolled iron and riveted together firmly. I had to erect a derrick to hoist them into place, but once in the cradle I had only to bind the two ends of each extremity of the long tanks to the short ones placed at right angles to them and I had the foundations of my boat laid. I bound the small tanks in place, as also the large ones, by bands of iron, several in number, which I brought together on one side by means of what is called a turn buckle, such as is often seen on iron bridges, both ends of the bands being formed with a screw-thread, and fitting into this turn-buckle nut on both sides, which could be then tightened by means of a lever, so as to bring an immense binding force upon each band.

Upon the outer edge of this parallelogram of tanks I had left a sort of comb of iron, some three inches in height, already pierced, or rather punched, ready to receive the roof of the boat, also air-tight, to be bolted to it, so that when all was done my platform of tanks would be nearly two feet wide within the boat, and allow me plenty of margin to rest any kind of a movable platform upon, or deck over the space that was left open, some fourteen feet long by six feet wide.

The nearest description that I can give of this roof is, that it rose in all directions at an angle of about forty-five degrees till it was bolted to a large flat surface made up of several sheets of rolled iron, which formed the top, which was ten feet long and four feet wide. This flat roof was fitted with a manhole, somewhat large in proportion to the rest of the boat, at least two feet square, and fitted over a raised rib of iron, which was packed with greased milkweed floss, and closed on the inside by set-screws, that were worked with a short iron lever, so as to make the opening perfectly air-tight.

I commenced this chapter by saying that I did not intend to make such a fool of myself as the old Robinson Crusoe did, and that I was not going to make any errors either of judgment or figures; and yet I had not my boat completed as far as I have described before I discovered that I had been a silly ass, fully as silly as it was possible for a mechanic to be, and one day it flashed upon me that my whole cradle, with its air-tight chests, was an egregious folly; that I had not the least need in the world for it, and that I had wasted time, labor, and patience in perfecting it. Carried away, as I was, with the means I intended to employ to sink and raise my boat I had totally overlooked the fact that as now being built, and as it would be launched, that it would float itself, the size of the four air-tight tanks being sufficient to float five times the upper structure built on top of them.

As I am writing a veritable history, and no fable, it behooves me to tell the truth, and it was with feelings of both mortification and mirth that I surveyed my partially finished work. It was the mental contemplation of a series of air-cocks, weights, pumps, etc., to be hereinafter described, that had led me astray as to the buoyancy of the boat as it now stood, and it was what I was going to use the tanks for, rather than what they now were, that had led me to this error. But then there was no great harm done. I had not to change the plan of the boat in the minutest particular, and the cradle might after all be advantageous in launching it, and preserve it from any casualty. Therefore, with the exception of my loss of time, I was nothing the worse; still I was rather crestfallen to think what a mistake I had made. But after mourning for a short time I set to work with renewed ardor to complete my task.

After having strapped the four tanks together and covered them with the iron roof, as described, I went on to complete the remainder of the boat, in this manner. In the interior, which I could easily reach by getting up from underneath the ways through two of the slats of the cradle, I arranged the following: The space in which I had to work was about fourteen feet in length, six feet wide, and eight feet high from the bottom of the tanks to the flat roof, which contained the manhole, which, for the present I left open, to give me both light and air. In the first place I connected all these four tanks together by means of a half-circular arm of piping some three inches in diameter, which I placed in each of the four corners of the parallelogram formed by the interior of the boat, leading from one tank to the other, where the latter met at an angle, so that the air that each contained was put in direct communication with the others. These connecting pipes were fitted in with a flange and riveted, and were placed a few inches from the bottom of the tanks, thus making really one tank of the whole. As the roof was fastened to the outside of these tanks, I had a seat or margin running round all the sides of the interior two feet wide, from the outer or further side of which arose the roofing. I could, therefore, easily lay any kind of a movable deck over this open space of fourteen feet by six feet, resting the ends of all my planks upon the top of the tanks in any direction.

Having connected all the tanks so as virtually to form one, so far as concerned being one air-chamber, I then went to work and pierced the perpendicular side of one of the tanks quite near the bottom and inserted a similar pipe to the horizontal ones that connected the tanks at the angles. This pipe, however, was in the form of a right angle, or rather its two ends were at a right angle, the bend being of a circular form. It pierced the tank near the bottom, as I have said, extended in a horizontal line some eight inches, and then gradually turned in a circular manner till the other end, about one foot in length, pointed downward, in an exact right-angle from the end entering the tank. This was put on with a flange, and made water-tight, and in the top of it, about three inches from the tank, was fixed a stopcock, with a long rod, which arose inside the boat, parallel with the side of the tank, till it ended in a handle, situated some ten inches higher than the top of the tanks. Near this, also, I erected another piece of pipe, which entered the top of the tank and pierced the roof of the boat, which was also fitted with a stopcock. Still another pipe pierced the roof, which was fitted with a stopcock outside as well as inside, and depended down into the boat some four feet from the roof. These four pipes, with their stopcocks, were so arranged as to be all near to each other, so that I could control them all without moving in my position, and were made at about the middle of what I called the starboard side of my boat, though it would be hard to say which side starboard was, as both ends of the boat were exactly alike up to the present time. But as I was eventually to have a propeller and rudder, which would define the stern, I had already concluded that the part of the boat nearest the water should be the bows, and hence I knew which to call the starboard side and which the port side. Added to the pipes and stopcocks already enumerated was one which was simply about a foot in height, which pierced the tank on the top, some few inches from the inner edge, and near the others. It was also fitted with a stopcock, and, that my readers may fully understand the uses to which I put all these appliances at a later day, it will be well, perhaps, to name them, so that when used it will be possible to understand to which of the numerous ones I refer; and to prevent confusion, and to make myself understood, I will say that the pipes at the angles of the tanks I took no note of, they not being fitted with any cocks, and only made to connect all the tanks together, so that any action I might make with any of the stopcocks would be communicated to the whole system of tanks, of which the foundations and main part of the boat was formed.

The pipes with stopcocks I named as follows: The one leading down into what would be the water when the boat was launched, and below the bottom of the tank some inches, fitted with a long rod and handle, I called the water-pipe and stopcock; the one that connected the tank with the roof, the tank air-pipe and stopcock; the one that pierced the roof and depended into the interior, the atmospheric pipe and outer and inner stopcocks; the one that stood erect, ten inches in height, the pump-pipe and stopcock. So that I had four pipes and five stopcocks to my boat, all of which had their uses, as shall be related.

Besides all these four pipes I also made near to them an opening into the tanks, which was fitted with a screw thread, upon which I could, when occasion demanded, erect a quite large and powerful pump, that I had made for the express purpose.

One more thing remained to be done, and that was to make all around the boat inside a sort of movable step, that would ship and unship. I was well aware that, unless the centre of gravity was kept well down, my boat would capsize and spill out all the air when in use, and to prevent this I made these movable steps, which it is difficult to describe. They were made of an upright piece of wood that was over four feet in length, and on the top of which another piece of wood was nailed horizontally, some twelve inches in width, like one arm of the letter T, whilst at the other end of the upright of four feet in length was nailed another horizontal piece, some twelve inches in width, on exactly the opposite side, like the letter L; so that when the whole was done the upper horizontal board rested one foot on the top of the tanks, whilst at the other end of the upright, two feet below the bottom of the tanks, was the other horizontal board, facing in towards the centre of the boat in all directions, and forming a kind of step or shelf, upon which weights could be placed so as to prevent all chance of the capsizing of the boat, the vomiting out of its air, and perhaps the destruction of its constructor and inventor. I had this so arranged that I could speedily ship and unship it in sections, for it was of course greatly in the way, and of no use except when the boat was launched.

I then completed my deck, which I made of light planks, marked and arranged so that I could readily board over all the space in the interior or leave part of it open. Upon further thoughts, some of this deck I made permanent, leaving only a space of about six feet by four open in the forward end, which I could cover or uncover.

I then entered upon another part of the programme, namely, the motive power by which I was to move this submarine monster, but that I had long ago solved in my own mind. For some months I had been practising two fine young goats upon a treadmill fitted to their size and strength, all the time having in view the end of using them to create the motive power of my boat; and for this purpose I had left the manhole two feet square so as to be able to take them down with me into it. I now went to work and transported the treadmill to the boat, and, having fixed it in place, I each day conveyed the goats on board and set them to work, so that they might get used to it. They were already used to the motion of the mill, and I noticed that with the precision of step of their race they worked the rounds of the mill much better than horses usually do, and they soon became accustomed to the boat and worked rapidly and well, obeying the least word of command. In fact they were to me almost companions, and it would be amazing to relate, if I had time, all I have taught these really sagacious and gentle creatures since I have been on the island; not these very ones of which I am now speaking in particular, but several of their race. Perhaps before I am through with my narrative I may give an idea of the many interesting things which I taught them.

For a long time I allowed the mill to be turned daily, without making up my mind just how I would connect it with the wheel or screw that I foresaw that I should have to make to propel the boat. I at last fixed upon a propeller, to work in the open space of water in the interior of the boat, and which I readily set up with good strong gearing, that I could as readily take down by hand when needful. By means of bevelled gearing I obtained several revolutions of my propeller to one of the balance-wheel of the treadmill, and I saw, as a mechanic, that my boat would move forward, perhaps not very fast, but still at the rate of three or four knots an hour, which would answer all purposes.

I had one more necessary thing to make, and that was a rudder, which I connected to the outside of the rear tank of the boat, bringing the tiller or steering rods into the interior of the boat under the bottom of the tank. I took care to fasten the heel of the rudder, which was quite wide, above the line of the bottom of the tank, so that if the boat grounded it would not be injured or destroyed.

And now I came to the most important part of my boat, and, in fact, upon the success of which, and practical application, rested the actual consummation of all my efforts. It was to obtain a supply of air whilst under the surface of the water without connection with the atmosphere, from which I was of course debarred. This problem solved, I had, I felt, the whole matter under control,— and let it not be believed that I had proceeded thus far in my self-imposed task without seeing a way out of this difficulty. The following every-day facts were easily ascertained from my Book of Useful Arts and Sciences, and upon the following conclusions I had based my invention. It is well known that oxygen is the portion of atmospheric air which supports life, and that it composes nearly twenty-two per cent of the same, whilst nitrogen, the remaining portion, is incapable of sustaining life. It is also well known that water also contains oxygen, in the proportion of two parts to one of hydrogen, of which two gases water is composed; or, in other words whilst atmospheric air holds only twenty-two per cent of the life-giving principle, water contains about sixty-six per cent, or, by weight, eight-ninths of oxygen to one-ninth of hydrogen. I also ascertained that the specific gravity of nitrogen is 0.94, whilst that of hydrogen is only 0.0692. Now if I could release the oxygen in the water I could make new air and at the same time precipitate the nitrogen and carbonic acid in the boat, that might be in the atmosphere, that had accumulated by my repeated breathings. Now the only problem to solve was evidently how to release this oxygen with which the water was so freely impregnated, charged, or made up of, and by the breathing of which fishes sustained life. And this is how I set about to do it. I made a very light paddle-wheel, full six feet in diameter, with many, but light arms, and only six inches across the face of each paddle; this was arranged so as to ship inside the boat, upon sockets arranged so that the lower paddles would just touch the water, and was adjustable by set screws, so that the journals could be lowered or elevated as the pressure of the water in the boat might show itself, higher or lower, according to the depth the boat might be at. By this arrangement I could have the paddles, which were more like a set of large-teethed combs than paddles, dip just such distance into the water as I desired. This wheel was connected by series of light wheels to the drum of the treadmill, so that I could obtain many revolutions of the water-wheel to one of the latter. My idea was this. By violent motion of the extreme ends of my comb-paddles through the water I intended to throw up into the interior of the boat a mass of minute spray, that in that form would itself release the oxygen that it contained, or at least a large part of it, and grant to my exhausted air the vitality it needed by new oxygen, or the life-sustaining principle, and at the same time precipitate the carbonic acid that the used-up atmosphere might contain. By this simple contrivance I intended to renew my air, and thus remain just as long below the surface as I might desire. The test that I should have that my air was becoming impure would be the dimness with which the candles would burn, with which I was to furnish the boat; and if after the use of the spray-wheel they again flashed up brilliantly, I should know that my theory was correct.

I had only one more thing to make to complete the whole affair, and that was a compass, which, having finished, I took within the boat to see and note its variations from the true north on account of the attraction of the iron, and to regulate it so that I might be aware always of my true course, for upon the exactitude of this instrument rested the responsibility of my ever again reaching land should I dare to go out into the ocean, supposing that the boat should work according to my desires and theory.

For light I had nothing but the light contained in the water and my candles. I could only pass from spot to spot by compass alone, and in case of utmost disaster plunge into the water within my own boat and try to reach the surface by coming up outside. It was not my intention to propel the boat near the bottom but only when near the surface. When near the bottom a turn or two of the propeller would send me in any needed direction.

A few blocks of iron to place upon my hanging shelves, and four anchors with strong rawhide hawsers, completed the appurtenances of the boat, and it was finished. By examination of my diary I found that I had been just nine months and eleven days in completing it from the day I had started to work upon the ways.

CHAPTER XX.

Launch the submarine boat. Experiment with it in Stillwater Cove.

HAVING completely finished and arranged my boat, my next task was to launch it and arrange for a series of experiments to ascertain its practical value. So one fine morning I went forth, with a beating heart, from the Hermitage, and waited patiently till nearly high water, and having greased my launching ways, and confined the cradle with a long and strong rope of rawhide, so that its momentum, when launched, should not carry it across Stillwater Cove without being checked before it reached the other side, I, with anxiety and almost fear, withdrew the iron bolts in front of it on the ways, and, going to the upper end, applied a crowbar to the still stationary mass, and after a few motions of the bar it began to move, and with one grand rush, not very fast, and yet majestic and striking, the cradle, with its precious freight, dashed into the water, and, being brought up by the long rope of rawhide fast to it, in a moment or two rested quietly upon its bosom.

I took the canoe "Fairy" and paddled all about it and saw that it sat well balanced, and secure, and that it floated beautifully. I then made fast to it with a short piece of rawhide rope, and commenced towing it to the mouth of Stillwater Cove, where the water was deep but smooth, to still further carry on my experiments. It was a good hard day's work to tow the heavy cradle to the place that I had fixed upon, which was at the mouth of Stillwater Cove, just within the breakwater, and about one mile beyond the landing-place and two or three miles from the Hermitage. This place was admirably fitted for my purposes, the shore being of a smooth sand and the water gradually deepening towards the centre of the cove. Nothing but clear, pure sea-sand on the bottom, and no rock to injure the boat or interfere with any experiment I might choose to make. Having arrived, I was glad to anchor the whole concern safely, and to make my way home in the canoe.

The next day, fitted out with all I thought I should need, including my two goats for the treadmill and provisions for a day or two, I made my way back again in the canoe to the floating cradle. I found everything all right, as I had left it, and proceeded to prove the practical efficiency of my invention. In the first place I took the goats on shore and tethered them, so that they could feed, but not escape. I then went to work and anchored the cradle in about twelve feet of water, it then being nearly low tide, or slack water. After having secured both it and the boat also, I went to work sawing off the slats of the cradle upon which the latter rested, and in less than two hours the last one was off, and I had the satisfaction of seeing my boat floating in the water, drawing only a few inches, certainly not over six, with the manhole open, sustained wholly by the confined air in the tanks, which held up the superstructure bravely. After the slats were cut away I drove out the pins from the mortised framework of the cradle and left my iron boat floating calmly on the bosom of the smooth waters of Stillwater Cove. Floating the timbers to one side that had formed the cradle, I allowed them to drift up stream with the now incoming tide, the boat being securely anchored by two anchors, one in advance and one at the stern, which were made fast to two ringbolts on the roof, placed at each extremity.

And now for my final test. I had made up my mind, if the thing was not a success, that I did not intend to be personally implicated in any disaster. Two things only could happen; one, that the boat might capsize, and if so I was prepared to go on board with little clothing, so that if it vomited me up I could easily reach the surface and then swim ashore, which was distant only a few rods; the other, that I should be unable to improve my air, once vitiated or used up. In the latter event I had only to dive out from under the boat and again make my way to the shore, losing, however, the lives of my poor goats.

I commenced my work by going on board of the boat by means of a short ladder, which reached from the manhole to the deck beneath. In the first place I shipped or hung the wooden shelves on each of the tanks, and loaded them with several iron weights, and also large smooth stones and the two anchors that belonged to the boat. This made it very firm, and sunk the tanks at least two inches more. I then went on shore and brought off my goats in the canoe and passed them on board through the manhole, which I had made large for this very purpose. I then went to work in the interior and fixed my compass, steering-gear, treadmill, and propeller, taking great care to see that my spray-wheel was all in order, and at hand ready to be hung.

I also conveyed on board some candles, flint and steel, matches, and provisions, and as the last thing took in the stern anchor, so that the boat lay with the tide, tailing up stream. The other hawser I conveyed also—by means of the canoe and with a boathook—under the forward tank, so that I held the end within the interior, and could cast it off at anytime. It was by the sun about eleven o'clock when I gave one glance around me, and, standing on the last round of the ladder, I drew the manhole cover over my head and commenced screwing it down on the inside, which having done I lighted several candles, although I had a fair light reflected from the water and the bottom of the cove, formed of white sea-sand, directly beneath me, and distant, I should judge by the state of the tide, some twenty to twenty-five feet. My goats had become so accustomed to the boat that they showed little surprise at the rather dim light, and stood ready to perform their part whenever I should put them to their customary task.

My heart beat rapidly, not with fear, but with excitement and expectation. Here I was, already shut out from the outer air, and in a little world of my own. I hesitated to complete my experiment, and before going further I turned to my provisions and took a good long drink of claret wine to strengthen my courage and steady my nerves. If I was in a scrape I could get out of it, but my poor goats! they, I was afraid, would have to pay for any error in judgment on my part. Having regained perfect composure, I made up my mind to make the first test of the practical value of my boat, and that was to see if I could descend to the bottom of the ocean, that lay beneath me. By moving around I felt convinced that my calculations about the centre of gravity had been correct, and I felt that the boat would not capsize. It was remarkably stiff and steady, and would, I felt confident, remain so when submerged. This bugbear was already off my mind, and gave me confidence to proceed. So, moving to the place on the starboard side where all my pipes and stopcocks were congregated, I commenced by opening the stopcock of the water-pipe, which, as I had foreseen, brought no perceptible change. Some little water rushed into the tanks, but only what was sufficient to compress the air to the extent of the weight of the superstructure of the boat. This experiment did not sink it one particle; its buoyancy remained exactly the same, for the same air remained in the tanks, although compressed, and was not able to escape on account of the position of the outlet of the pipe that had opened communication between it and the water, pointing, as it did, directly to the centre of the earth. After waiting a little, and seeing that this all worked well, I placed my hand upon the stopcock of a more important pipe, namely the tank air-pipe, which led from the tanks to the outer surface of the superstructure.

Now, or never! Upon turning this cock I should descend or my theory would be incorrect. The moment my hand opened this valve the air would be expelled by the pressure of the boat upon the water, conveyed to the air in the tanks by the water-pipe, which was already open; and, as it was expelled, so the buoyancy of the boat would be decreased, and I should descend. The fatal moment had come, and with a firm hand I opened the tank air-pipe, and plainly heard the escaping air, the incoming water, and felt the boat descending, and saw the sandy bottom apparently approaching me. I cut off the discharge of the tank air-pipe, and with a slight rebound the boat arose again a few inches towards the surface, simply regaining its true position in equilibrio, that it had for a moment passed, by the momentum of its descent. By little turns of this stopcock I discovered, as I expected, that I could move the boat in a descending direction even an inch at a time. The movement was a perfect fascination, but each delivery of air was bringing me nearer the bottom, and as yet I had tried no means of rising again to the surface.

When I had gotten to within about six feet of the former I thought it time to see if I could again rise towards the surface. I was well aware that, having used up this air, it was so much loss to me, but I was in hopes to be able to replace it; and even if I could not replace it to make the boat rise to near the surface without it. I could do this in one way, by casting overboard the anchors and weights lying upon the wooden shelves; but this, if done to any great extent, might cause the capsizing of the whole affair. No; I had a better way than this, and at it I went. In the first place I closed the water-pipe, and then, having opened the screw-valve in the connected tanks, I screwed upon it the pump and commenced discharging the water from them—that had run in to take the place of the discharged air—into the water of the ocean, which formed, in one sense, the interior flooring of my boat.

To make this pump work I of course opened, and left open, the pump-pipe, so that the air from the interior rushed in and filled the tank as fast as the pump discharged the water, and at each stroke of the pump, after the first few, the boat, as I had hoped, began to rise; the water, having been just so much ballast to carry it down, being discharged by the pump, was just so much thrown overboard in weight to allow it to rise. By persistent pumping I made my boat rise quite near the surface, but not to the buoyant position it at first maintained, for I had in my descent used up considerable of the air in the tanks, which I had as yet not replaced, or rather what I had used from them had been replaced from the air of the interior when I pumped out the water, which I could only do by allowing the connection between the tanks and the interior to be open, so as to make the pump work. In short I had lost just so much buoyancy as was equal to the escaped air; but still I had been able to make the boat descend and ascend.

These experiments took me over two hours, and I commenced to feel the need of new air, and to notice that my candles began to burn a little dimly. I was thus warned that my air was being used up and charged with carbonic gas, and that it was time for me to renew it. So I unscrewed the pump and closed the valve, opened the water-pipe, and placed my hand upon the tank air-pipe and prepared to descend. One effect I should have noticed of my loss of air, and that was that the water in the interior of the boat rose considerably, and a large portion of the tanks was now submerged. A few turns of the stopcock of the tank air-pipe carried me near to the bottom, where I desired to be, to try my last and most important experiment.

Arriving to within a few feet of the bottom I rigged my spray-wheel, and connected it with the drum of the treadmill and set the goats at work. And it was time, for my breathing had become oppressive, and the animals themselves seemed dull and frightened. I had waited almost too long. My candles also commenced to burn more dimly, and I prepared to take my plunge into the water and come up outside of the boat should my experiment now fail. But wonder of wonders! my spray-wheel made but a few revolutions, dashing large quantities of minute spray into the interior by its rapid motion, before my lungs were relieved, the candles renewed their brilliancy, and the goats recovered from the lassitude under which they had a moment before seemed to be laboring.

The problem was solved. I had made my own air. I could remain below the surface as long as I desired. Everything about me was rather damp and moist from the dashing of spray about the interior, and several of the candles, that I had not protected, were put out; but two, in the extremity of the boat, were preserved, and now that my problem was solved I did not again light the former, the two remaining ones being all-sufficient. And in fact I did not need them; my own lungs, I found, were sufficient as a guide to tell me in future when to renew the air. Still it was fascinating to see these two candles burning brilliantly that had but a moment before been so dim. The reflected light from the pure sandy bottom just below me was amply sufficient for all purposes.

I imagined, by the slight shadow that the boat cast on the bottom beneath, from the brilliant sun that I knew was shining overhead, and from counting up in my mind all I had done since leaving the surface, that the air had lasted me, as nearly as I could judge, two hours; and that seemed to be the extreme limit to which I could go and not renew it. I also knew by the quantity of tallow consumed in the candles that it must be nearly that amount of time. I also noticed that the spray-wheel had not only purified my air, but that whilst it was in operation the boat had slightly ascended, proving that I had gained a lighter gas for the nitrogen and carbonic acid precipitated.

One more thing remained to be tested, and I should feel that my labors were complete. In the first place I made the boat ascend as far as possible, by means of the pump and stopcocks, as before described, and then I went to work and rigged my propeller and set the goats at work. I got the boat as near the surface as possible before communicating motion to it, so as not to run against any obstacle if possible. But then the body of water in which I was submerged was so pure, and free from anything of that nature, that there was little danger after all. With a feeling of confidence that I had not had in all the other experiments, I cast off the hawser affixed to the anchor that held the boat, and started the goats. Mechanics did not trouble me, and it was with no surprise, but only gratification, that I saw by the bottom that the boat was moving forward, and that it readily obeyed the helm. I turned it completely around by the tiller, and made an excursion of fully half a mile, I should think, up Stillwater Cove, once in a while getting out of the channel, when by stopping the goats and reversing the propeller I was able to back into the channel again, and finally to turn around by a series of forward and backward motions till I again arrived at the place from which I had started, which I knew by the anchor lying in mid-channel. By observation of the bottom I should say that the boat was propelled at least three miles an hour, which was sufficient for all my purposes.

After arriving back to my first position I pointed the boat towards the sandy beach, and when the hanging shelves touched the bottom I carefully removed them and their weights to the top of the tanks, in the interior, and, with a short pole, pushed the boat still nearer the shore, till the tanks rested on the sand; and this I did with care and quickly, for I was a little afraid of a capsize when the hanging shelves were removed, which was only for a moment or two, however, before the boat was at rest on its own foundations, on the sand. I then forced down under the water from the interior quite a large block of wood under the tank that had the water pipe protruding, so that the latter should not be hurt by being driven into the sand when the whole boat was stranded at low water.

The tide being now at ebb, I knew that I had not long to wait before the whole boat would be high and dry upon the sand. But having gotten my piece of timber under the tank to protect the water pipe, I opened the atmospheric pipe and let the whole boat sink solidly to the bottom, in all its parts, as well as the forward part that was resting on the sand. I then cautiously opened the manhole, ready to close it immediately should it yet be below the surface; but, as I supposed, it was out of the water at least six inches, and, throwing it open, I once again emerged into the open air of day.

I released the goats and carried them on shore, and as the tide receded all the water left my tanks through the water pipe, which I then closed, and there was my boat as buoyant again as when it was first launched, with all the tanks full of air, and ready to be towed to an anchorage as soon as the next incoming tide should float it.

I lay down upon the sea-side and contemplated my work, and wondered if it would not make me a rich man if I could transport it to some civilized portion of the earth. Was it possible for me to make a boat of this kind on a large scale, with a team of goats, fifteen or twenty in number, and traverse the depths of the ocean till I arrived at some Christian land? One thing at least was in its favor: I need fear no storms or any dangers of the ocean from waves or wind, and one other great obstacle would be overcome. I could leave the helm at any time and go to sleep, feeling sure that my boat would not be driven about by waves and winds, but repose peacefully in eqilibrio till I again awoke, and forced it forward upon its passage.

There was matter for great thought in all this. But on the other hand, should my air fail me, or my tanks leak, or steering apparatus get out of order, I should either be stifled to death, drowned, or left beneath the ocean to wear out a miserable existence till death relieved me. The risk was too great. Besides I had no means but a compass of ascertaining where I was going, no glass lens to give me any light; but perhaps I might possibly make the latter. It was all well enough for me to venture out from my island where at the worst I could escape and swim ashore; and, if the truth must be spoken, I found myself too much in love with my island, and all its comforts, to hazard too much to escape from it. I cannot say that I did not long and long to escape, and that I did not mourn for companionship; but I must also confess that I had begun to love my island home also, in one sense, and I could see far enough ahead now into the future to acknowledge to myself that, should I escape, it would be only to return with companions to here end my days.

These were different feelings than what I had when first cast on the island, as will readily be perceived by perusal of this manuscript, if ever, by the mercy of God, it comes to anybody's hands to read. But what could I—an old sailor, but not an old man, who had banged around the world—ask for more than I could obtain on my island except companionship? Nothing.

Having secured the boat, and put the goats and spare traps into the canoe, I at the close of the day paddled myself back to the Hermitage, determined on the morrow to make an excursion out of Stillwater Cove into the ocean, and see what I could discover. To be doubly secure I made up my mind to tow the canoe with a long rope of rawhide on the surface of the water, astern of the submarine boat below it, so that if I did meet with disaster or shipwreck I could get into the former and make my way to the shore in safety,—in fact this arrangement would take away all danger from the enterprise, as I felt confident that I could always escape from the boat, and it would be well worth while to have the canoe at hand to jump into, if I had to do so.

CHAPTER XXI.

Explore the bottom of the ocean in the vicinity of the island with my submarine boat. Discover pearl-oysters, and invent a great improvement to my boat.

I AROSE early the next day, and started in my canoe, accompanied by my two goats, to the mouth of Stillwater Cove. It was a beautiful day, and one just suited for my purpose. I had made up my mind to make my way out of the cove into the open ocean, and along the coast line of the breakwater, taking care, if possible, not to get too near in, so as to be troubled with the undertow. To enable me to do this I was first obliged to land on the breakwater, and with my compass to lay out some of the bearings and directions of the land and shore line—so as to be able to make a kind of chart—upon a piece of birch bark that I had brought for that purpose, to enable me to find my way back into the cove, or, missing that, at least to bring up somewhere on the shores of Perseverance Bay. Having gotten everything arranged, I went on board of my boat, which I found floating and in perfect order, having first recovered my anchor in the stream and taken that also on board. Once in the interior I shipped the hanging shelves and distributed the weights in their usual places. My goats evidently took everything as a matter of course, and quietly remained where I had fastened them, near the treadmill. I put my movable deck in good order, saw that my fresh water, provisions, and candles were all right, with a bundle of hay for the goats also. I then carefully examined all the stopcocks, the steering apparatus, and spray-wheel, and finding everything in order, and a fine, sunshiny day overhead, I made fast the "Fairy" to a ringbolt on the outside of the boat, and paid out a long scope of rawhide rope, so that I could sink at least forty fathoms without drawing her after me. Then, giving one more look at everything, and lighting a candle in case I should need one in any emergency, I shipped my propeller, attached the band to the treadmill, cast off my moorings, started the goats, and got under way, standing out in a westerly direction into the ocean.

As soon as I was clear of Point Deliverance, and when about a hundred fathoms seaward to the eastward, I changed my course to the northward, all this time moving along with the manhole wide open, out of which I often looked to see how I was proceeding, and in what direction to steer. But I had scarcely got the head of the boat to the eastward before a heavy sea broke all over me, and came dashing down the manhole, but did me no harm, falling back, as it did, in the interior, into its own element. The inside deck was rather spattered, to be sure, and the goats evidently began to be surprised, if not frightened, at the motion of the boat, and I saw that the time had come to submerge it; but I kept on, for I was determined to keep above the surface, if possible, till I found myself opposite the place on the breakwater at which I had first been cast on shore, and which I well knew; for it was there that I determined to make my first descent, and see if I could not find some remains of the articles that were in the whaleboat when I was cast away. So to keep out the water I closed the manhole cover, but once in a while ran up the ladder, opened it and looked about me, till I at last found myself opposite the spot, and not more than a quarter of a mile distant.

I then, by a word, stopped the goats, and shut down the cover of the manhole, and screwed up the set-screws, opened the water-pipe, and placed my hand upon the air-tank stopcock and allowed some of the air to escape. In one instant the boat that had before been buffeting about upon the billows was as quiet and steady as a rock. I did not descend far before I shut off the escape of air, and sat down to think. In the first place I saw that by a series of experiments I could easily, in the future, tell just how far I was descending by the rise of the water inside of the boat upon the sides of the tanks; for, as I descended, the pressure upon the air was of course increased, and therefore compressed, so that the water rose higher within, and nearer to the movable deck.

Having examined my compass I started the goats again, and made for the outside of the breakwater, hoping to strike the very place where the whaleboat had formerly been destroyed. As I advanced towards the shore I found that I was not deep enough down to see the bottom, so I again descended till I could plainly see it below me, not ten feet distant. I spoke to my goats and had them relax their speed, and moved slowly forward. The bottom laid out to my view was composed of sand, rocks, and an infinite variety of sea plants. How can I expect to convey to anyone the beauties of this submarine view. The water— by its transparency and the light that I obtained by reflection—could not have been more than six fathoms deep, and in fact I knew that it was in that neighborhood, for I had often, in my canoe, been outside of the breakwater before, fishing and for other purposes, and I knew very nearly what water I ought to have.

Although anxious to explore I could not resist the temptation to stop and gaze upon the beauties that lay before me, in all their marvellous freshness, unseen before by the eyes of mortal man since their creation by the Almighty. Many of the plants before me, that seemed like sparkling gems, I knew well would look so only as they now stood, in their native garden, surrounded by water, and that, taken from the element or cast on shore, would fade ten times quicker than any land plant. Fishes of various sizes darted in every direction, and simply to please my own conceit I deliberately dropped a line amongst them and captured several, which I again allowed to escape. But even in my own solitude I could not help smiling at the idea of a mortal man sailing along at the bottom of the ocean and capturing its denizens at his leisure,—the thing was too comical.

Although I had stopped the goats, my boat still had a motion, or rather I should say that I could see that the tide was drifting it sideways to the northwest, but very slowly, not more than a knot an hour. I think that I could have sat hours and looked upon this scene. It was like a new world opening up before me. Everything was plain, for no ripple blurred the surface of the water in the interior of my boat, and no wind of heaven rushed over it to destroy, for a moment even, its transparency. It was as still and motionless as death, and as quite large rocks and new objects seemed to pass by below me, I was sometimes startled at their beauty and grandeur. It was a panorama. I seemed to be stationary, fixed, as immovable as the foundations of the earth; and these objects passed in review before me exactly as if moving along in space. It was difficult to disabuse my mind of the fact that I was not stationary, but that the objects upon which I was gazing were. This feeling was increased in a marked degree by the absolute stillness and want of motion, in itself, of my submarine boat.

I hated to break in upon this deathlike silence by the motion of my propeller, but I was being swept by the tide slowly away from my destination, and it would not do to proceed too far, so as to lose the true course by compass. Reluctantly then I spoke to my goats and put the boat in motion, and proceeded upon my way. I had not advanced, far when I perceived that I was entering a perfect forest of submarine plants and kelp, the long tendrils of which, sustained by the water, reached upwards towards the surface. I saw that I was upon dangerous ground, and therefore stopped the treadmill and reversed my propeller, and backed out from my position. I then rigged my pump and made the boat ascend so as to pass over their heads, and again forced the boat towards the breakwater, but this time I found that I was getting into the undertow, and the forest beneath me warned me not to descend; so I had nothing to do but to back out seaward and give up all idea of exploring the place of my shipwreck.

When I had pushed back so as to be clear of the tangled plants that seemed to surround the margin of the island on this side, I commenced again to descend, and allowed the boat to rest within a few feet of the bottom, and, rigging my spray-wheel, went to work to renew and purify my air, which I had no difficulty in doing. I then moved about in different directions, taking care all the time to keep a reckoning by my compass of the courses sailed and the distances passed over, by dead reckoning. During one of my stationary moments I had a complete view of as large a shark as I have ever seen. He passed directly beneath me, and took no more notice of the boat than if it had been a stationary rock. He was at least sixteen feet in length, and would have made but a mouthful of poor me.

THE SUBMARINE BOAT.—Page 243.

I wish that I could describe the sights that I saw. It seemed as if I was in another world, and had passed from this existence to one more advanced, in which I floated in space. The extreme silence of all about me, and the rigidness of all objects seen, was very striking. At each moment some beautiful fish or plant struck my view, of which I had never before had any knowledge. I moved about in all directions, trying to find, if possible, some bank of pearl-oysters, and I had a good idea of how they ought to look, for I had once, in my younger days, descended with the divers in the East Indies to the pearl-oyster beds, and knew the whole practical science of the business. At last, at a point by compass and dead-reckoning about northeast from Point Deliverance, and distant two miles, I came upon what I wanted,—or rather what I hoped was what I wanted,—namely, a perfect bank of oysters, in thousands, clustered together. My first act was, after stopping the boat, to throw over a light anchor, to hold it in position; the next to cast into the water a small grapnel, to which was attached a long piece of rawhide rope, fully forty fathoms in length, ending in a wooden buoy, shaped like a tenpin in a bowling-alley, and of about the same size. This, after dropping the grapnel, by means of a short boat-hook I thrust under the tank of the boat, and saw it rapidly take up the spare line as it ascended towards the surface. And as it was so ascending it flashed upon me that here was also a practical way of determining at all times the depth of water; for this buoy only took out about seven or eight fathoms of the line before it became stationary, evidently having reached the surface. I used this buoy to anchor the reef, so as to be able to find it in future trips, when I had only to stand out towards it, on pleasant days, on the surface of the water, and, when I found it, descend and find myself on the reef.

And for measurement of my depth below the surface I had only, in future, to fasten a light, buoyant piece of wood to a small cord, marked off into fathoms, which I could at any time thrust under the tanks and allow to ascend to the surface, and note how many of the fathoms of line were taken up, which would denote my depth below the surface, and then draw my sounding-buoy back again into the boat for further use, simply reversing the method that is used on shipboard. That is to say, instead of throwing a lead with a marked line to the bottom of the ocean, I threw a buoy to the surface. Nature seemed to be capsized, and everything upside down, as used to appear in using the inverted telescope in my first attempts to take the altitude of the sun with a sextant. If I had not lived so solitary a life I could have laughed at many of the things that befel me in this submarine boat.

Having gotten the boat securely anchored, and the buoy thrown out as I have related, I went to work gathering the oysters. I had taken care to bring with me a light pickaxe, a crowbar, and a sort of hand-rake, similar to ones used by East Indian divers, which I proceeded to employ upon the mass of oysters below me. I had no difficulty in detaching all I wanted of them, and filling my decks, and particularly the hanging shelves, which I relieved of their stones and weights, replacing them by masses of the oysters. I made a long job of this, and, having gotten all I desired, I drew up my anchor and got again under way, ascending as near as possible to the surface before advancing towards the land. During all this time, whenever necessary, I had renewed my air by use of the spray-wheel.

Being near the surface, which I was made aware of in several ways, such as the increased light, the disappearance of the bottom from view, and a slight noise of the waves above me, and a little motion of the boat, caused by their agitation, I put the goats at full speed, feeling sure that for at least two miles nothing was in my way. After I had, as I calculated, gone this distance, I slowed down, and proceeded more cautiously; but after an hour's work I made no land, nor found any great shallowing of the water. Here was a pretty scrape. By my chart I was past Stillwater Cove, and even in the interior of the island, and not a sign of the land or shallow water could I find. I began to be seriously troubled, and I foresaw that unless I soon made some shallow water I should be obliged to dive under my tanks, and look about me and see where I was. But before I did this I descended and anchored, and found out for the first time that I was at last in a strong current, setting towards the westward. This frightened me still more, and I ascended at once, stripped off the little clothing that I had on, and plunged into the water and came up buoyant as a cork on the surface, and pulled the canoe towards me and got into it without much effort. One glance showed me what the trouble was. I had gradually, during the whole day, drifted to the westward, and had passed West Signal Point, and was, in the direction I was pursuing, leaving the island on the port hand, behind me. One glance in the open air cleared my brain, and gave me a true idea of where I was, for I confess that the many courses that I had sailed beneath the surface had rather confused me.

Taking one more good look about me, I plunged into the sea under my tanks, and was again inside my boat, which I speedily started in the right direction, and in less than two hours made shallow water, when I once more had to dive out of the boat and look about me, when I found that I had made a pretty good landfall, as I was in Perseverance Bay, not more than a quarter of a mile from the mouth of Stillwater Cove, having overrun it; and as I was so near home I dove back again, started the goats, and soon had the pleasure of finding myself in the cove, some part of the bottom of which I already recognized; and I foresaw that if I should make many trips I should be able to recognize the bottom just as easily as one recognizes familiar objects on land.

I stranded my boat in the usual manner, and waited for the tide, which was now at an ebb, to leave the top exposed, for the buoyancy of the boat was not very great from my frequent use of the air-tank stopcock. During this time I busied myself in casting the oysters to the bottom, and then moving the boat, which was thus lightened, a little to one side, so that, when the tide returned, the former would be exposed clear of the boat. I then unshipped the movable shelves and put everything in order in the interior, and sat down and ate a hearty meal, after which I tried the manhole, which, by the pressure of the tanks upon the sand, I felt confident was above the surface, which proved to be the fact. I soon had the goats ashore, who seemed to be glad to escape from the confinement of the boat, and gambolled about me. I waited patiently for the tide to go down far enough for me to get at my oysters, which I conveyed to the land, above high-water mark, and, sitting down, commenced with my knife to open one or two of them. I think it was the third that I was opening when my knife-blade struck against something that made my heart beat. I laid open the oyster, and there within it, nestled near to the upper shell, was as beautiful and perfect a pearl as anyone could desire to see. It was not very large,—perhaps the size of a common pea,—but of a pure cream color, and of perfect oval form. I knew at once that it was a jewel of value and price, and I carefully hid it away in my clothing. This prize sufficed me. It proved to me the importance of my discovery, and I was determined that the sun should do the remainder of the work for me, and therefore left the oysters where they lay, to be made putrid by exposure, when the pearls that they might contain could be very easily washed out.

I was not wholly satisfied with my boat. I did not like the idea of having to dive overboard to find out where I was, as I had had to to-day, and I commenced racking my brains to overcome it; and at last I accomplished it in theory, and it may be as well to state here that it served me perfectly when put in practice on many future occasions, and in fact almost took the place of the spray-wheel. It was this. I arranged, in the first place, a sort of air-boat, in the shape of the half shell of an English walnut, but shallower, nearly four feet in length. This boat was made of very thin sheet-iron, but perfectly airtight, and upon it was lashed, in a horizontal position, a cylinder of sheet-iron, closed at one end and open at the other, a foot in diameter, and in length the same as the shallow, airtight, walnut-shaped boat that sustained it. At the end of this boat, just below the mouth of the cylinder, was affixed a solid iron ring, and to this was spliced a strong rawhide rope of great length. To utilize this machine I made two long bars of iron, which I could arrange in the interior of the boat, across its greatest diameter, in the form of the letter V, pointing downwards towards the bottom of the ocean, and at the point of contact was arranged a block through which the rope attached to the air-boat could be rove. This inverted derrick, in the form of a letter V, was still further braced by another bar, leading to one of the short diameters of the boat, in the interior, forming a tripod. To use the air-boat I had only (at any time when beneath the surface and in need of air, either to purify that surrounding me or obtain enough to force the boat out of water on the surface, after having used up the air in the tanks) to reeve the rawhide rope through the derrick, as above, and erect the same in an inverted form, pointing towards the bottom, and then put the air-boat in the water in the interior of the submarine boat, force it bodily down in a horizontal manner till the cylinder was filled with water, and then start the goats so that the rope attached to the nose of the air-boat, leading down to the inverted apex of the tripod, through the block, and thence to the drum of the treadmill, would be tautened, and cause it to erect itself in a perpendicular manner, and be forced down under the water towards the apex of the tripod. When submerged enough to clear the bottom of the tank I slackened the rope gradually, pressing it at the same time out and clear from the tank, and yet keeping enough strain upon it to prevent its touching the latter; when, as soon as it was clear, I slacked the rope wholly, to allow it to arise to the surface outside, which it rapidly did on account of the confined air in the air-tight shell. Of course immediately upon its arrival at the surface it righted itself, and presented the appearance, on a small scale, of a barrel with one head out, placed in a horizontal position upon a small sled or vessel. In this position all the water that had been in the cylinder was at once discharged, and, to get a measure of fresh air exactly equal to the dimensions of this cylinder, I had only to set the goats to work, to take the rope to the drum of the treadmill, the first effect of which was to depress the nose and open mouth of the cylinder on the air-boat, at the surface, and the next to drag it down under the water in a perpendicular position, with the cylinder charged with air, which could not escape. As soon as it appeared clear of the outside of the tank, against which it rubbed in its descent, and was brought down near to the inverted apex of the tripod, I commenced slacking the same rope till it arrived at the surface of the water within the submarine boat, when I cast off the rope and it righted itself violently, discharging at the same time the contents of the cylinder in the shape of new air, and I had only to repeat this process of conveying fresh air from the surface to obtain all I needed, taking care only, in sending the apparatus to the surface, to see that, when the air-boat was first pointed under water ready to ascend, it took back with it none of its precious freight, which was easily obviated when it was held in a semi-perpendicular state, and half submerged ready to ascend, by pushing upon the part out of water till it was forced into a horizontal position, the air from the cylinder discharged, and replaced by water, when, after descending towards the connecting points of the tripod and pushed clear of the side tank, it was allowed to ascend to the surface, discharge the water, and descend again filled with air.

With this apparatus I found that I could even compress the air in the interior, and in many future expeditions I had no trouble in making my submarine boat, at any time, self-sustaining on the surface of the water, and I could by a little labor come to the surface, open my manhole, and look about me and see where I was.

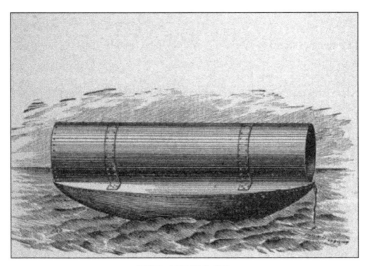

THE AIR BOAT.

CHAPTER XXII.

Manufacture glass. Build a steam yacht, and circumnavigate the island. Lay up large stores of valuable pearls obtained from the pearl oysters.

AFTER I had perfected my submarine boat I used it often to gather the pearl oysters, and it was not difficult to steer straight to the buoy on the reef, fill the shelves of my boat, arise again to the surface, and return home. After allowing my first load to putrify, I went to work upon them and washed them out in the water of Stillwater Cove, obtaining nearly a handful of seed-pearls, some twelve of the size of peas, and four very handsome and perfectly-shaped larger ones. This induced me to keep on; for here was portable wealth such as I could take away with me when I left the island. Let it suffice to say that, during repeated trips at intervals, I ended by obtaining probably the finest private collection of pearls in the world. I had some eighteen of enormous size, nearly as large as English walnuts, but as perfect as if from the turning-lathe,—except one that had a slight blemish, and one that was irregular in form,—and I much doubted if there were more perfect and larger ones in any royal crown. They were regal in size and appearance, and were, I knew, of immense value. Besides these sixteen perfect gems without price, I had at least four hundred and sixty as large as a small filbert nut, and several hundreds as large as common peas, not to speak of vast quantities of seed-pearls, too many to enumerate. If I could escape from the island, these treasures would keep me in ease and comfort in any part of the world.

During the year succeeding the finishing of my submarine boat, I was taken up with many new inventions almost too numerous to mention. I enclosed another large piece of ground as a pasture for my goats, of which I had now as many as I chose to keep; in fact, I loosed many of the she-goats and kids into the woods to return to a state of nature, having more than I could attend to. From the remainder I made cheese, butter, jerked meat, etc. It may be possible that some persons have lived as well as I, but at this time I had everything that could be desired. I improved upon my ways of preserving my fruits, and from a ground-nut that I found on the island extracted a most delicious oil, which I used in all my cooking. I had by this time, by repeated breedings, brought the wild quail, that I saw when first arriving at the island, to a state of barnyard fowl, and I had their delicate flesh and eggs added to my larder. From my grapes I was able to make several kinds of pleasant light wines. In fact I had everything but companionship.

But by my temperament I could not keep still, so I must yet invent something new that would be of use to me. What I wanted most at this time was glass, plate-glass for my submarine boat, and I was determined to have it. So, with my book to guide me, at it I went. I knew that silicic acid, practically glass, was represented by sea-sand. I also knew, or rather discovered from perusal and study of my book, that this sea-sand, freed from iron, formed the base of glass. Also that silica, silicic acid, or oxide of silicon exists in great abundance in nature, being the principal constituent in rock and stone, and that crystal and quartz held it in its purest forms. This, combined with potash or soda, and subjected to a powerful heat, would, I knew, make glass, if mixed in the right proportions.

In the first place I gathered some five or six hundred pounds of the finest, purest, and whitest sea-sand that I could find. This I carefully washed in some seven or eight waters of Rapid River, till it was purified of all its salt, and then it was placed in my ore-cleansing kiln, and burned, or rather heated, to a red heat, to get rid of all vegetable matter, and then sifted through wire screens to get rid of any pieces of fuel with which it might have become charged. Having thus gotten my sand all in order, purified, and cleansed, I went with the goat team, and a handy little cart with cast-iron wheels and frame, that I had made during odd times, to the coal mine, to bring home some of the chalk there to be found, of which there were large quantities, and of a fine quality. This I brought home and reduced to a fine powder by pounding it up with hammers, and sifting it through fine sieves. I then went to work and built some large fires upon the seaside, upon which, when in full blaze, I placed large quantities of kelp or barilla, which was finally converted into ashes. After I had burned sufficient of it, I allowed the fires to go out, and gathered the ashes carefully, to which I added a quantity of fresh water and stirred it about carefully, preserving the fluid in open iron pans, which I placed upon fires and evaporated, and had carbonate of soda as the result; and, although on a desert island where there is supposed to be nothing, my book informed me that kelp or barilla was the best article from which to make carbonate of soda, and some kinds of sea-sand the very best base of which to form glass. Having thus procured the component parts of which to make my glass, I set to to make a large clay pot in which to fuse it, that would fit in the base of my iron-smelting furnace, so as to be surrounded by the air blasts. My clay pits fitted me out with this without any trouble, and I then had to manufacture a level plate of iron, about two feet square, with a raised rim of some inch and a half in height, and this I placed in a horizontal position in front of the door of the furnace, and rigged above it a large iron roller to work by machinery, that could be passed over its face. I then mixed my ingredients by hand in the following proportions:—

Prepared sand   400 lbs.

Carbonate of soda 250 "

Ground chalk   30 "

and put the empty clay pot into the furnace and started an immense fire around it. As soon as it was at a white heat I filled it with my mixture, placing it in the pot by means of a long iron spoon some six feet in length, protecting my face with a mask of goatskin, and my hands by gloves of the same material. When vitrification was complete, which took place in about eighteen hours, and which I ascertained by plunging a long rod of iron into the pot, I ladled out a lot of the mass by means of a clay-lined, long-handled, iron ladle, and poured the rapidly-cooling but pliable substance upon the iron table constructed for it, and, pressing the iron roller upon it in all its parts, soon rolled out a sheet of glass two feet square and at least an inch and a half thick. Allowing this to cool, I repeated the process after removing it, till I had made six large squares. I then changed the roller so as to come lower down to the iron plate, and by this method commenced turning out sheets of plate glass two feet square and about one quarter of an inch thick. My task was done. I had all the glass I should ever want as long as I should live; enough for the side lights of my boat, and also for windows to the Hermitage. Fully satisfied with my task, I allowed my fire to go down, and the large slabs of glass to cool.

On the next day I set to work to polish the glass I had made, and this I found a laborious and slow task. But it had to be done, and I commenced with fine pulverized and sifted sand, or rather quartz, and ended with chalk. It was many weeks before all was done, for I needed emery to help me in this task, and could find none, and had to make other things do. But at last I had four fine slabs of plate glass quite well polished and clear, each two feet square, and one and a half inches thick; and several that were of a quarter of an inch in thickness, many of which I had broken in attempting to polish them. The latter were soon fitted into position as window lights in the Hermitage, and pleasant enough they made the interior look. The former were made to fit into four holes cut out of the solid iron of the boat and fitted with flanges, into which they were set with great care by means of what the Chinese call *chenam*, a sort of water cement made of lime, oil, white of eggs, and clam shells powdered fine, used by them in making all their vessels water-tight. These four panes of plate glass, each two feet square, and an inch and a half thick, were placed at either end and both sides of my boat on the slanting roof, and gave me a chance to see in what direction the boat was moving, to avoid obstacles, and aid me in submarine navigation. They were also thick enough to withstand a blow of great force, and not to be affected by the pressure of

150

water upon them when at great depths; but, to preserve them more fully from any danger, I built outside of them all a wire screen, the meshes of which were perhaps two inches apart, and distant from the face of the glass outwards some six inches, made of strong iron wire at least three eighths of an inch in diameter, so that if by chance the boat should receive a blow, or be forced upon or back against any object, these screens would receive the blow and not the naked glass, although I am ready to believe that the latter would have sustained an immense shock without breaking, it was so thick and perfect, without crack or flaw. I should have said that all my glass had just the faintest tinge of green, caused by the minute particles of iron in the sea-sand of which it was composed, of which I had not been able to completely free it, although I had used magnets to extract large portions of it; but enough remained to give it this very light tinge of which I have spoken.

I had no difficulty in cutting my thin glass into any shape I desired, by means of case-hardened steel, which would scratch it deep enough to be broken off, although a glazier's diamond would have perhaps performed the operation better; but a piece of sharp-edged chilled-steel answered all practical purposes. Later on I had occasion to again make glass, but at this time I did not waste a moment in making household utensils, glasses, or bottles, my earthenware, wooden ware, and ironware doing excellent service for me, and I had need of no utensil that they could not supply.

With my submarine boat perfected and supplied as it now was with its immense windows, I made many trips, and the sights under the water that my eyes gazed upon I could write thousands of pages about. I made no great discovery, however, in all my wanderings, except to find two more oyster-banks, more to the northeast than the first one, but not so prolific. I saw often many creatures that never come to the surface, and for which there is no name, some of them small and seemingly harmless, and others quite frightful and startling. I passed over, upon three different occasions, enormous cuttle-fishes, or squids, with tentacles at least six or eight feet in length, and eyes three inches in diameter; but they never, upon any occasion, paid the slightest attention to my boat, but remained perfectly motionless, clinging to the stony bottom, waiting for their prey, and I took good care never to disturb them. Immense crabs and lobsters, the very patriarchs of the ocean, often lay on the bottom to my view, and seemingly deformed and curious fishes, large and small, some like serpents and some like inflated balls, often met my view as I floated along with the tide a few feet above the bottom. I never wholly got over the sensation of being at the bottom of the ocean; it always seemed as if I had entered another world, where all was changed, and in which every living thing was compelled to keep an eternal silence.

Many parts of the bottom, especially that near the pearl-oyster reef and the approaches to Stillwater Cove, became, shortly after using my glass windows, as familiar to me as similar places would have been on land; there being fully as many distinguishing marks, peculiar in themselves, as upon the rocks and protuberances of the island itself. I loved this lonely under-water drifting about, and indulged in it as a recreation as well as to increase my store of pearls. I sometimes watched for hours the habits and movements of the animals below me, that seemed not to care for my presence; but quite often some huge monster of the sea would pass by me, making me hold my breath with awe, if not fright. But I often thought that my iron boat would be a hard mouthful for anything beneath the waters to attempt to swallow.

I had long, long ago given over any idea of being attacked by savages, and my nerves had become again, as in my younger days, hard as steel; yet I often used to think of how I could lie concealed in this boat, beyond discovery from any source, should I ever be attacked, or how, rising to the surface amongst a fleet of canoes, I could spread dismay by my appearance alone from the bottom of the ocean, among any body of savages, however numerically strong or valiant.

No one will ever know the gardens of the ocean that I often sailed over, more beautiful far than anything upon the earth.

My restless energy did not stop at the consummation of this submarine boat, but during this year I went to work upon a beautiful small steam yacht, to use for my pleasure and recreation. It was built partly of wood and iron, and constructed upon the ways from which the submarine boat was formerly launched. This steam yacht was not very large, but it was of a fine model and graceful lines. I built it twenty feet in length and six feet in width, and three feet draft of water, with nearly the whole decked over except the cockpit aft. It was fitted with one long mast, situated near the bows, and only to be used in case of emergency. The building of the boiler and engine, of about four-horse power, was to me a pleasure, not a labor, and the casting of the screw was the only thing that gave me any trouble. But this I finally overcame, after a few trials with different moulds. The little house that contained the cabin and engine-room was lighted with small pieces of plate glass, and I fitted the interior with a nice cot to sleep upon, lockers for provisions, coal, and fuel, a small cast-iron stove for cooking purposes, and all the handy appurtenances of a small yacht. My sail was not a very elegant one, and was made out of strong matting, light but coarse; I having, as yet, not attempted to make cloth in any shape. My cable was of rawhide, and my anchors, of course, of iron.

With this boat, after a preparatory trial of its engine, in company with one of my pet goats I set out upon the circumnavigation of my island. It was one fine

December morning that I steamed down Stillwater Cove, the yacht moving rapidly and evenly along through the water, and the machinery and screw working well and smoothly. I had invented a sort of comb to retain the tiller in any given position whilst absent from the deck in the engine-room to put on more fuel or oil the engine, so that the yacht would proceed in a straight course till my return to the deck. I intended to make a complete circuit of the island, and to be absent several days if needful; so before leaving the Hermitage I put everything in order. As to my flocks and birds, they at this season could take care of themselves very well for a few days. I laid my course first for West Signal Point, and, when I had doubled it, I pointed the yacht due north, and made quite an excursion in that direction, fully twenty-five miles; but, as I suspected, found no sign of any other land, although I climbed upon the mast and looked about me in all directions, the island astern being in the dim distance. I found that my little yacht was a splendid sea-boat, and, decked over as she was, plunged into the waves of the Pacific unharmed. Its rate of speed, in smooth water, I estimated at fully nine knots, and in a seaway at least five or six. Having in vain looked about me for land, which, however, I did not expect to find, I put about and steered back to the island, leaving West Signal Point on the port hand, and close aboard, making my way to the southward, and parallel with the western shore of the island, distant not over one mile.

When off Penguin Point I again put to sea, at least twenty-five miles due west; but as in the former case discovered no land. When I had again come up with the island the day was nearly spent, and I took the yacht into a small cove, just to the westward of Mirror Bay, and, having anchored in smooth water, ate my supper, played with and caressed my goat, and went to bed. In the early morning I again got under way and stood out to sea, to the southward, but no sign of land. Thence I proceeded to Eastern Cape, and from there made a trip seaward, to the eastward, but with similar barren results. From thence I made my way home to the Hermitage, pleased with my yacht and with the trip, but doubly convinced that my island was alone and distinct, and not one of a series or group. As I passed Mirror Bay on this trip I was tempted to enter it and explore the island more fully in that direction, but as I found on the second day that my machinery of the yacht needed some slight alteration and change, I made my way home, as I have said, determined to make a new trip for this very purpose, and therefore, upon my arrival, I immediately went to work upon those parts of the engine that did not exactly please me by their working, and improved and perfected them in my workshop, by means of my turning-lathe and other tools, till they suited my mechanical tastes and worked perfectly to my satisfaction. I fitted my yacht with two nice iron howitzers, of about three pounds caliber, and had hung up in the cabin a harpoon and lance, with two of my smooth-bored guns and plenty of ammunition. The coal that I had stored on board would last me many days, for there was at least three tons, and the furnace of my little boiler did not use more than one-quarter of a ton daily, if as much. I had also on deck a very light small boat, not over six feet in length, in which I could reach the shore whenever I anchored the yacht near it.

Thus fitted out, which took me several days, I started again upon my exploration, and it was upon this trip I made one of the most startling discoveries yet since I had been shipwrecked; one that changed all my views about the island, and the future, and carried me completely out of my every-day life into a period of excitement, curiosity, and amazement, and which, as will be disclosed, had a marked effect upon all my future movements.

CHAPTER XXIII.

Discovery of a human habitation. The skeleton and manuscript.

It will be remembered that I had never been able in my own mind to account for many things that I had found upon the island; amongst others, the goats, sweet potatoes, and tobacco. I could not disabuse my mind of the impression that some one else had been before me on this lonely spot of earth; that man at some age of its existence had placed his foot upon the soil. I little knew when I started on my trip to Mirror Bay how soon some of these mysteries, that had so many years confused me, would in a moment be made plain. I looked forward to no startling adventure, and yet I was, without knowing it, sailing straight towards the solution of many problems, guided, unknown to myself, by a mightier hand than mine.

I arrived safely in Mirror Bay, and proceeded up towards the river, the machinery of my yacht working beautifully. When I arrived at the mouth I found that I could still ascend, but thought it best to anchor near the western bank, just inside the mouth, and not a stone's throw from the bank. I had come by the way of the Eastern Cape, and having started early in the morning, at daybreak, about four o'clock, I found myself at anchor at about seven o'clock by the sun, having made the run in three hours, or at least six knots an hour, the distance being, as near as I can judge, eighteen miles.

When my yacht was nicely anchored, and the fire put out and the engine placed in order, I took my little flat-boat and went on shore with my goat, intending to walk inland in a northwesterly direction, towards Mirror Lake; but I had scarcely taken ten steps into the open woods before I recoiled with a sensation of fear, such as I have never before experienced, and made for my boat, but before I reached it my horror had become curiosity. Turning about, I faced the direction from whence I had come; and, taking my shot-gun from my shoulder, I looked carefully to the flint to see that it was all right, eased a knife that I carried at my belt in its sheath, and thus, with my mind collected, but with my brain almost confused with excitement, I advanced slowly towards the place from which I had just retreated in so startled a manner. Yes; there could be no mistake; looking through the boughs of an intervening tree of small growth, I saw a HUMAN HABITATION, and the habitation evidently of a civilized, or at least semi-civilized, being. Before me—in ruins, to be sure, but still unmistakably the work of human hands, and skilled ones, too—stood a stone hut at least ten feet square, and with dilapidated stone walls at least eight feet high, without roof, and with evident remains of a door and two apertures for windows facing towards the sea in the direction I stood. I leaned against the tree that I stood near, faint and overcome with emotion. A thousand thoughts rushed through my mind, but I soon convinced myself that this habitation had been deserted by man for long ages of time. Should I ever know how long? Everything about the hut denoted extreme age and decay; trees were even growing from the interior, and showed above the walls where the roof ought to be; rank weeds and grass grew in the open doorway, and vines crept around the dismantled walls; yet there it stood, a monument unmistakable of a human presence at some previous time, and a civilized one, too. No savage hands ever erected those walls or pierced those apertures for door and windows. I sat down, still gazing at the hut, and tried to gather my wits together and to overcome my agitation. Fifteen minutes in this position brought to me a certain amount of composure, for nothing presented itself that I could fear, and it seemed as if little information could be gained by a closer inspection.

Those who had built this hut had long since departed whence they came, or were stilled by the hand of death; there was nothing left for me,—no companionship, no information, nothing but the knowledge gained that the island had been inhabited either by chance or by colonization, and those who had visited it had built this hut, and, no doubt, brought the goats, tobacco, and sweet potatoes that had so long puzzled my brains to account for. Was this hut all, or was it one of a series? Was it the preparatory discovery to many others, or lone and solitary? Alas! I knew not.

Having completely recovered my composure and stilled my beating pulses, I advanced to examine more minutely the cause of my amazement and fright. Passing within what had formerly been the door, I found myself in a space of at least nine feet square, enclosed within rough, strong, but ruined walls. The remains of shelves were plainly visible upon the walls, and evidences of a prolonged occupation at some former day by civilized persons met my view. The hut had evidently never had any flooring, and in its place a long and luxuriant grass flourished. Passing further into the interior, I moved towards the southerly wall—the door opening towards the eastward—and proceeded to examine that portion. My eye caught, half way up the wall, a sort of projecting shelf, with something evidently made by human hands still clinging to its battered and weather-worn surface. I rushed eagerly towards it, but, before my hand could grasp it, I was almost thrown down by catching my feet in an obstacle hidden in the long grass, between me and my object. Regaining myself with difficulty, I glanced down to see what had obstructed my progress, and found my feet *mixed up in the bones of a human skeleton.* I was not frightened, but shocked, and, clearing my feet with care, I stepped back and examined these mute witnesses of former life. Here then, thought I, are the remains of one at least who has lived and died upon my island long ages ago. How did he come here? How long did he live here? Why did he die? Would this eventually be my fate, and should I some day have to lie down and die, too, with no one to inter my bones? This human being was either alone or else the last to succumb, or otherwise his bones would have been interred and not left to whiten the surface of the earth. Would this be my fate? To be sure, I had not as yet been sick one day so as to be confined to my bed, and had only suffered from minor ills, such as colds and slight summer attacks, but how long was it to be before I should be laid up in my own house, with fever or delirium, with none to care for me? To be sure, I had carefully arranged affairs about my bed in case of such a contingency, having arranged a shelf, upon which I had placed simple remedies, such as I had been able to collect, near to my hand, such as sulphur and saltpetre, with a few steeped herbs enclosed in jars ready for use to my hand, with spare matches, and lamps, and some preserved suet, etc. I had done everything that I could do to preserve myself should I be taken suddenly and dangerously ill; but what was to prevent me from at last coming to this very state before me, to die in my bed, and remain a grinning skeleton for some future generation to discover. Nothing but Divine Providence could keep me from this pitiable end. For if I did not escape it was only a matter of time when I should appear before others as this poor mortal appeared before me. I could not and would not believe that I was reserved for so cruel a fate. I was unwilling to believe that God, who had endowed me with enough intellect to construct and invent the many useful articles I had gathered around me, would allow me to perish, alone, uncared for, and unwept. My courage arose as I gazed upon the skeleton before me, and I moralized thus: You must have lived in an age when God had not granted to mortals the permission to discover and utilize many of the arts and sciences of my day; you did not live when steam was the motive power, when the lightnings of the heavens were made obedient to man to convey his demands and requests, when the paddle-wheels of floating steamers beat the waters of all the oceans of the earth. All of these things, and many others, were unknown to you. My case is not as bad as yours was, if you were shipwrecked. I, of this century, on this same island, have gathered about me, from nothing, strength and power. You, seemingly, have had only this rude hut over your head. I have chances of escape; I doubt if you ever had any from the first day of your arrival, for I cannot conceive of your having willingly remained upon this desert isle. And now, poor mortal, passed away so long ago, let us see if you can do anything for me, your living prototype.

FINDING THE SKELETON.—Page 268.

And, thus ending my musings, I kneeled down and commenced cutting away with my knife the long grass that surrounded and that was even interwoven with the bones. The clothes, if there had ever been any at the time of death, had long since been destroyed and blown away by the winds of heaven. From the narrow bone of the middle finger of the left hand, which was nearest me, I drew off a handsome gold-chased ring, with a fine carbuncle for a jewel, the whole in a state of perfect preservation. This at once announced that my unfortunate was a civilized being and one of some importance. Moving towards the right hand, I found the bones of the fingers imbedded in a tuft of grass, and, releasing them, I ascertained that they grasped some object in their clasp, which remained partly buried in the ground and soil that nature had piled up around it. Taking the point of my knife, I released it, and held in my hand a beautifully chased silver snuff-box, encrusted and soiled by exposure, to be sure, but in a remarkable state of preservation. I forced open the lid, and took out a small piece of parchment, which almost crumbled under my fingers. Being, however, warned by my discovery, I acted with caution, and took the box and its contents to a smooth stone outside the hut, and commenced examining the contents with care. The wrapper of parchment that crumbled under my fingers disclosed another within it that was much better preserved, and, noticing carefully that there was no writing upon the outer covering, I cast it away and commenced opening the second, which was also of parchment, but in a good state of preservation. This was also blank, but within it was enclosed a third piece, not more than six inches square when opened, on which were written these words:—

Anno Dom. 1781,

Dec. ye 17th.

✠

Being neare to death I putt this on record in hopes that some God-fearing mann maye find it and become my heir. I have burried under ye foot of ye large tree, distant 27 pases from ye sou-yeste corner of this hous, a fulle and complete hystorie of my life and where my treasur lyes. Alas! at ye bottom of the sea, but hence it maye by skill and fortytude bee recovered.

Who he be that redes this, if of Christan breeding, I proclaim heir to me. If not Christan I hope he wille nott be able to read this, or discover my secret. Lette my bones be burried. My curse upon himn who uses this treasur butt for good, which I acquired by yeares of bloodshed. Wille God ever forgive me?

THOMAS SUTLAND.

As I finished reading the above I glanced out beyond the ruined walls, and saw before me the tree that was mentioned, but I did not move to solve the mystery further. Here was matter enough for thought before me where I sat. What had been this mortal's life that he should here set down that he had gained a treasure through bloodshed? I examined carefully the ink with which the document was written, and made up my mind that it was composed of blood, that this human being had probably written these lines with blood from his own veins some eighty years ago; and, although the characters were faint, they were perfectly legible. Treasure! what was treasure to me that was at the bottom of the sea? Ah! but I had a submarine boat with which I could seek for it. My curiosity began to be aroused, but my thoughts were still so conflicting that I did not yet fully grasp the information that the parchment conveyed.

After a long musing I commenced again my search around the hut, and, in the first place, took from the shelf the article that had attracted my notice, which proved to be a perfectly formed clay pipe, of heavy and ancient pattern, but as well preserved as the day it was laid upon the shelf. The stem, of whatever material formed, had disappeared, but there was the bowl, just as used eighty years ago. I put it carefully to one side, and again commenced my explorations of the hut, which I began, by clearing away all the grass and shrubbery from within, and exposing, as far as practicable, the former flooring. Suffice it to say that, after a long day's work, this was the amount of my discoveries and collections,—one rusty gun-barrel, with stock and lock gone; the rusty remains of two large pistols, and one cutlass; the remnants of an iron pot, and open fireplace; and parts of a steel-plated helmet or fighting hat; with smaller pieces of iron and steel, of which it was impossible now to distinguish the use or form, a golden ring, a silver snuff-box, a pipe, a mass of useless, broken, rust-eaten steel and iron utensils, and a human skeleton. This was all, when gathered together, that my explorations brought to view, except the precious document that was to explain the whole. With a sad and despondent heart I called my pet goat to my side, and descended towards the yacht, and went on board to think over my strange adventure. This island then had been known eighty years ago, had been inhabited, even. Had this unfortunate been cast on shore alone as I was? No; his arms, hut, and utensils told another story. Why had he remained in this solitary spot? To expiate some horrible crime? By the confession before me, it seemed like it. How much character did this parchment, on the face of it, proclaim? In the first place, a bloody and savage nature, by its own confession; second, a fair, but not over excellent, education; third, a superstitious or cowardly fear of the Almighty in the hour of death, after confessed deeds of blood; fourth, a love of display, as exhibited in the snuff-box and ring; fifth, authority and command of some degree, as shown by the remains of costly weapons. Thus I gave my brain excitement all the night, instead of indulging my curiosity by trying to discover the history referred to. My life had been so lonely that I postponed as long as possible the final revelation of the life of this man. I played with the sensations that my discovery had evoked, as a cat does with a mouse, or as a sailor with his last piece of tobacco at sea, or a miser his gold. The sensation was so intoxicating to have something to think about out of the usual run that I did not choose to have it solved, and yet was on fire to solve it. In the morning, after a restless, sleepless night, I plunged into the waters of the bay and took my customary bath, and then to breakfast, after which I commenced the proseecution of my search with vigor. I proceeded to the southeast corner of the hut and paced off twenty-seven paces, which brought me to the tree that my eye had already picked out as the one alluded to. With some iron utensils that I had brought from the yacht, including the iron coal-shovel and poker, I commenced making an excavation in the ground. I dug a hole at least four feet deep before I found anything out of the ordinary, but when at about that depth, my shovel struck upon something that was not earth, as I felt assured, and I soon laid open before my eyes the top of what was evidently a wooden box of some foot or two in diameter, but so interwoven with the roots of the tree that had evidently grown about it since it was placed there, that I was unable to extricate it. I therefore went on board of the yacht and returned with a hatchet, and soon cleared away these obstructions, and dragged to the surface a rough wooden box, of an oblong shape, made of wood, of at least two inches in thickness originally, but now worm-eaten, rotten, and ready to be broken to pieces with my hands alone. With a slight use of my hatchet I forced this carefully apart, and found, within, a package rolled in what had evidently at some former time been birch bark. Peeling this off, I came to a glazed earthen or porcelain pitcher or jug with a large mouth and with handle, that would hold at least two quarts, the color of which was a dirty white or dusky brown. The mouth of this jug was closed with parchment, once carefully tied down, but now in a state of decomposition. Grasping my prize, I went on board of my yacht to examine it more fully at my leisure. This whole adventure had so worked upon my nervous system that I even went to work and got up steam and buoyed my anchor, ready to cast off at a moment's notice, before I would proceed further with my examination. Why I did this I cannot tell. It was a sort of sailor's precaution, engendered by years of care and prudence. My reason told me I had nothing to fear; my nerves told me to get ready for any emergency.

Having seated myself quietly on deck, after making all the above arrangements, I took the jug again in hand and commenced to tear off carefully the parchment at the mouth. The outside one, being removed, disclosed another in a better state of preservation, and this second a third, which, when removed, showed a large soft-wood plug or cover, fitting into the mouth of the jug, and profusely covered with a sort of pitch, which had evidently been melted and poured upon it, and was probably made from the resinous gums with which the island abounded. I soon had this started by repeated knocks of my knife-handle, and the plug exposed, which, with the point of my knife, I had little difficulty in extracting; having done which, I emptied upon the deck a roll of parchment, tied up with a broad band of the same material. With intense emotion I opened the roll, consisting of several sheets; and, written in black ink, but with similar errors and ancient spelling, as in the first document, I found the following, which, corrected into modern English, read thus:—

CHAPTER XXIV.

The Pirate's Manuscript.

ISLAND IN THE PACIFIC OCEAN,

October, 1781.

IN grief and sorrow, and great bodily pain, I write these lines, fearing that I shall not recover from my wounds, and that death will soon seize upon me. I ask Christian burial for my bones, and that God will forgive me my many sins.

I was born an Englishman and passed an adventurous life till, in the year 1778, I found myself, after a life of villainy and piracy, captain of the armed brig "Rover," at the age of thirty-three, and cruising in these seas. It would take too long and be of little interest to relate how through years of bloodshed I had arrived at this eminence. It is enough to say that for the last ten years of my life I have spared neither man, woman, nor child, and that God in his power has at last brought this retribution upon my head. I could relate scenes of horror, and hairbreadth escapes, that would not be believed or credited, therefore I skip them all and come to the causes of my being imprisoned on this desolate island. The brig that I commanded had on many occasions been successful in preying upon the Spanish galleons of this coast, and many a South American city had even been put under contribution; but to the immense wealth and plunder thus obtained was to be added still another capture. On the morning of the 14th of August, 1781, the brig "Rover" lay in near the coast of South America waiting for the passage of two galleons, loaded with treasure from the Northern mines of El Dorado, for Valparaiso. From spies in that city I had found out that the treasure was estimated at twelve millions, in gold and silver bars, and that these galleons were armed with six eighteen-pounders each, and with a crew of Spaniards and natives, numbering sixty men. Two long weeks had we been lying near the coast standing out in the morning, and in towards the evening, waiting for our prey; when, on this fatal morning, after heading seaward for four hours, we discovered the enemy on the horizon to the northwest. The "Rover" was a strong, well-built brig of three hundred tons, and was manned by one hundred and twenty human devils, drawn from all nations, but mostly Englishmen, with a few South Americans and natives. We carried eight eighteen-pounders, and one long thirty-two pivot gun amidships. Our vessel was fast and a splendid sea-boat. We were favored with a wind from the southeast, which put the enemy to leeward of us, and we boldly clapped on all sail to come up with him, which perceiving, and also that we had the weather gauge, the cowardly Spaniards put up their helm and kept off before the wind, hoping to outsail us; but before they commenced this manœuvre we had approached near enough to be sure that they were what we had been waiting for, and therefore, rigging out stu'nsails on both sides, we bowled along before the wind to the northwest, after the retreating enemy.

It was soon apparent that the "Rover" was the faster sailer, and also that one of the galleons was a much better sailer or better handled than her consort; for we were coming up hand over hand to one of them, whilst the other, some two miles ahead, held her own much better. As we neared the sternmost and lagging galleon, we commenced firing from our bow-chasers, but without apparent effect. I think to this day that if the two had kept together they might possibly have beaten us off, but, separated as they were by their own cowardice, they would, I felt convinced, fall an easy prey to our designs. As we gradually neared the galleon, the crew of the "Rover" became more and more excited; and the cursed thirst for gold, and subsequent license and revel that was sure to follow its acquisition, glowered in each countenance. The time had come for our usual unholy rites, and, ordering up the steward, the usual cask of brandy was hoisted to the deck, the contents poured into two large tubs, and one of them transported to the quarter deck, whilst the other was left at the main hatch, and, at a preconcerted signal, the two bow-chasers were discharged at the enemy, the black flag run up to the mizzen peak, and all hands called upon to splice the main brace, or in other words, to craze their brains by partaking of the fiery liquor poured out before them; the quantity on the quarter deck having been mixed with gunpowder, to be distributed at the guns during the coming conflict as I might deem best or proper. We were now rapidly advancing upon our prey, but none of our shot seemed to have taken effect and as yet she had made no reply.

Commanding silence fore and aft, I ordered more sail crowded upon the "Rover," and stood on till we were nearly alongside, and not a gunshot distant, and then, having brought all the eighteen-pounders to the starboard side, had them loaded with grape and canister. I ordered in sail, running in all the stu'nsails, and clearing the deck for action; but at last the enemy seemed to have waked up, for, whilst this was being done, she poured into us her broadside, killing and wounding several of the crew, but doing no further damage, and then immediately came to the wind, close hauled on the starboard tack. We followed rapidly, but, as all the guns were on the starboard side, I ran under her lee rather than try to keep the weather gauge, and at short pistol distance sent the contents of eight eighteen-pounders into her sides and rigging. The result was to have been anticipated: down came her top hamper and light sails, and she lay a wreck upon the water. Shooting ahead in the "Rover," I shortened sail, and, crossing her fore foot, held my vessel with the main topsail to the mast and poured in six broadsides of canister and grape, raking the enemy fore and aft, to which she could not reply with a single gun, and at the termination of which she lay a complete wreck upon the bosom of the ocean. Without a moment's delay the main yard was squared away, and, turning upon her heel, the "Rover" made all sail for the other galleon. It was four hours before we came up to her so as to be within shot, when a discharge from our pivot gun cut away some of her top-hamper, so that we commenced overhauling her rapidly; but this one, although she had run away in the commencement, now evidently meant fight, and she replied to our broadsides with bravery and vigor, so much so that I saw that there was nothing for it but to board her and carry her by assault, as we were being cut up in a fearful manner, and my crew dropping at each discharge. Seeing this, I sung out to the helmsman, "Lay her alongside," and, with a crash, we in a few moments struck her fore chains, having the weather gauge, and in a moment were securely lashed together. Mounting the taffrail, I sung out "Boarders away," and jumped upon the deck of the galleon, followed by my crew. It was with the same results I have so often seen before: no mercy, no quarter, and down under the blows of the cruel Rovers soon fell the Spaniards, and the galleon was ours. It was time, as she was evidently commencing to leak badly. Some of the crew were ordered to the pumps, and the main hatch was burst open, and, under threat of instant death, the position of the treasure was pointed out by the Spanish captain. The amount, estimated at some seven millions, was passed by sixty hands as fast as possible to the hold of the "Rover," down the companion way; and, when all was over, freeing the brig from the galleon, I took position near to her, crashing into her broadside after broadside, till she, with her wounded, dying, and living, sank beneath the waves. We had scarcely finished our awful work when night set down upon us, and, taking the bearings of the other wreck, we moved slowly forward toward her under shortened sail, so as not to pass her in the darkness. Upon mustering the crew it was found that twenty-seven had paid the penalty of death, whilst seventeen were seriously wounded, and twenty-one slightly.

When morning broke, there lay the other galleon, not one mile distant broad on our weather bow. We soon came up to her and saw that she showed no signs of life, and, hauling off, we commenced repairing injuries that we had suffered in the conflict with her consort, and, having everything in as good order as possible, ranged up alongside preparatory to boarding, and in fact made fast with grappling-irons to the wreck; but not a man opposed us. Pouring in upon her decks, and questioning the wounded still on board, we ascertained that all remaining alive—not over twenty in number, it seemed—

who were not wounded so as to be unable to do so, had escaped during the night in the shallop and made for the coast, trusting to the mercy of the sea rather than to ours. We soon had the bullion we were after exposed to view and rapidly transferred to the "Rover," which amounted, by the reckoning of the wounded Spaniards, to about five millions, so that the "Rover" had actually under hatches the enormous weight of some eighty tons in solid silver, and twenty-five tons in gold, all in bars, so as to overflow the usual stronghold and necessitate stowage in the hold, as one might stow cargo.

Having helped ourselves to all the casks of wine and brandy on board, we cut adrift from the wreck, and in spite of the cries of the wounded upon her decks, by numerous well-directed broadsides sent her to the bottom of the ocean, where dead men tell no tales. After this horrid crime was perpetrated, we set sail upon the "Rover" to the southward to avoid any vessels that might be sent for our capture, as I made up my mind that we should keep well to sea and out of the way of all traffic till search for us had been given up. To this end I steered in a direction out of the track of all known land, till on the 15th September, in the morning, we discovered this unknown island dead ahead, and, finding that it showed no signs of being inhabited, I passed around to the southward and eastward to see if there was a good bay for anchorage, determined to allow the crew to go on shore and have their carouse, if such was the case. We soon opened this bay, where this is written, and, having sent a boat on shore and ascertained that there was good fresh water and evidently no inhabitants, I brought the "Rover" well into the bay and anchored her in six fathoms.

This being done, a detail of the crew was made to build this hut for my accommodation. The weather being cool, and thinking that we had found a splendid stronghold for the future, I commanded several goats to be landed, and as my men strolled hither and thither they were instructed to plant a sweet potato once in a while, of which we had plenty on board, and some seeds of the tobacco plant were also planted, I believe, at nearly the other side of the island, near some river. I made up my mind that this should be our rendezvous in the future, for I could not find the island put down upon any chart, and I believed it utterly unknown. I made known my resolves to my subordinates, and they to the crew, which seemed to please them much; and now, having gotten everything in readiness and a watch set aboard the vessel, casks of brandy were hoisted from the hold and landed upon the island. To these were added a large stock of provisions; and an enormous tent was erected of spare sails. Details by lot were made of men to cook, and a watch to keep guard in the vessel, and then for three days all discipline was relaxed, and drunken orgies too fearful to be related commenced, at the end of which a new detail of the most sober was made for the watch on the ship and the cooking, when the same recommenced. During these six days I withdrew with one servant from all this into this hut that I had ordered built, and passed the time as pleasantly as I could, with trips once in a while to the vessel and back. Each day I received the usual report of so many men killed in drunken brawls or so many wounded; but I never moved a finger to stop the affray, feeling that this was the best way to allow them to work off their bad blood and passions. It was, however, on the seventh day that I saw cause for alarm, and, alas! too late. I had noticed that there seemed to be some trouble brewing, and that my second in command, when he came to make his daily report, had not the air of respect that he used to have, and that the reports of serious fights were more frequent than on former carousals of a similar nature. Why, here were some five men killed and seven wounded since we had been on the island, and upon inquiry I found that they were all men whom I knew were devoted to me, if a pirate may use that term. All at once it flashed upon my brain that my second in command was inciting the crew to my downfall and his own elevation. In fact, the matter was made too apparent on that very day; for, after hearing the report, I was sitting at the door of this hut when an unearthly confusion and din commenced at the large tent and the air was filled with the report of pistols (all guns being positively forbidden on shore), and shouts and cries of men in terrible earnest mixed with the screams of the wounded. I buckled on my cutlass and picked up my two pistols, and, calling upon my servant to follow me, made for the tent; but before I arrived there I was met by a retreating body of my men who were making for my hut, crying out, "Treason, treason, treason!" followed by another portion of the crew, at the head of whom was my second in command, all disguise now thrown off, cheering his part of the crew on to my destruction. I gathered about me the retreating men loyal to me, and we faced the rest. The first man who advanced I shot dead, the second also, and the day had almost turned in my favor when, with a well-directed pistol-shot and with a curse mingled with the report, my rival brought me to the ground, the ball having passed through my chest and out at the back. I fell to the ground, and in one instant my prestige of years was gone. When I say gone I mean that it was so far gone that it barely saved my life, for the men still stood quite firm upon my side, when, with the wit and talent worthier of a better cause, my rival moved between the conflicting lines and called for a truce, uttering at the same time the following words: "Now look a-here, shipmates, what is the use of our cutting each other's throats any more? There lies your late captain, still alive to be sure, but good for nothing more. I am bound to be captain of the 'Rover,' and you see I have more men to back me, and a head to them also, than you have. What's the use of our cutting each other's throats when we have some ten or fifteen millions to spend? If you don't like to give in I only admire you the more for it; and if you will join my side and lay down your arms, I promise before you all not to injure one hair on the head of our late captain, but to leave him here on this island without further molestation. Come, that is a fair offer. You have done enough for honor. Do you accept? Why, who have you on your side that can navigate a vessel? Who will give you as much liberty and money as I will? We will live in common, and have no more of this damned supposed superiority. But as for Captain Sutland, dead or alive, he and I can't sail in the same vessel again. I will do all I say, and swear it,"— and amidst the wildest cheers of excitement and drunken enthusiasm, I found myself lying deserted and, as I believed, bleeding to death. After some little hand-shaking and congratulations, however, I was, by order of my rival, carried carefully to this hut, where my wound was examined by the doctor and proclaimed not necessarily mortal. Food and water in profusion, fuel for my fire, and anything that I should naturally require during my convalescence, should it ever take place, was, with the reckless generosity of sailors, piled up near me; and with a few farewells from some who really cared for me, I was left alone, my whole crew, under the command of their new leader, working like beavers to take down their tent, get on board and to sea, and thence to some haven of rest, where they could as quickly as possible squander the wealth so criminally acquired. They had placed me upon my wooden bed, so that I could look out of the open window upon the bay and ship, and see their departure. It was nearly sundown before they had everything ready, and with a heavy heart I heard them at work weighing the anchor, leaving me alone to solitude, my outraged God, and probably death.

SHOOTING THE PIRATE CAPTAIN.—PAGE 286.

Lying on my bed of pain, I saw the topsails mastheaded and everything made ready for a start, and as the sun sank to rest in the west, shedding a glow upon the waters, the "Rover" got under way and stood out to the southward and eastward, leaving me upon this desolate island to live or die. I knew what would be the eventual end of their reckless career, for I knew that the pirate who had superseded me, although of great animal courage, had very little education, and that he was wanting in the art of practical navigation. The sun had not been down an hour before the whole heavens changed their appearance, and dark clouds from the southward commenced to overcast the stars. The wind began to moan amongst the trees, and the sea to give forth that solemn sound or breathing that often forbodes a storm. In less than three hours it was blowing heavily from the southeast, the direction the vessel had taken to clear the island, and exactly opposite to the light northwest wind that had in the first part of the evening wafted her off the island's coast. At midnight it was blowing a hurricane, and still I gazed from my bed through the open casement towards the sea. There was not much rain, and what there was did not reach me, my bed being some distance from the window of the hut. At this time, in spite of my misery and the fever of my wound, I, after drinking a draught of water placed beside me, fell asleep, or rather dozed, from which I was awakened by the sound of guns,—yes, great guns. Wounded, feverish, as I was, I moved in my bed to glance into the outer darkness. The tempest was raging with increased fury, and as I looked into the inky blackness seaward, not more than four miles distant as I should judge flashed the discharge from a cannon, and in a moment after, the dull but deadened report met my ear. I kept my eye fixed upon the spot, for I knew that, if it came from anywhere near the same spot again, the "Rover" was on a reef, and that there would be little hope for her. In a few minutes another flash occurred, and I saw that it was in the same situation. Good God, and had your retribution met them then so suddenly? I saw in my mind at once the actual state of affairs as readily as if I had been on board.

The "Rover" had stood to the southeast with a fair wind, and all the crew under their new master, being without discipline, had allowed themselves to be caught by the gale from the opposite direction with all sail set, or too much at least; that she had either been taken aback and lost her masts at once, weakened in previous conflicts, or else, before she could be squared away before the blast, been cast on her beam ends, and for safety had had them cut away. After which, unmanageable with a drunken crew and an incompetent master, she had drifted in the trough of the sea, back slowly but gradually towards the anchorage she had just left, until, brought up upon some sunken ledge outside the harbor, she was pounding out her life upon the jagged rocks concealed beneath the water. This was, I felt, the case, and would any be saved to be my companions on this desolate island? I knew that not a living soul would be left to tell the tale. The mighty roar of the wind and the noise of the surf on the beach, with the groaning of the trees, extinguished all hope.

No more firing was heard, and nothing but the blackness of night surrounded me, and the cry of the angry blast filled my ears. I became insensible and fell back in my bed without life or motion. When I again opened my eyes, the light of a bright spring morning flashed upon them, and although the wind had gone down, the angry rush of the surf was still to be heard thundering upon the shore; and there, yes there, not far at sea, and plainly beneath my sight, and in full view, lay part of the hull of the once famous "Rover," dismasted, dismantled, and beating her ribs out upon an outer bar or reef. I saw that she could not last long, and that no human being could have survived the preceding night. I should have said that, before the pirates sailed, they had buried the men who had been killed upon the island; but I saw plainly that many bodies would now be swept on shore that would never see Christian or any other burial but that of the white, glistening sands of the beach, and the maws of insatiable sea monsters; whilst I thought even, the vessel was fast breaking up under my eye, each mighty wave, hitting her seaward bulwark, was thrust high into air, passing over and burying her in an ocean of spray and water such as no handiwork of man could long resist. At each succeeding appearance, masses of the hull had disappeared, and it was only a question of time how soon some twelve million of dollars in gold and silver, guarded by a crew of some eighty resolute men when in their senses, who had gone before, would be buried in the ocean forever. I could not take my eyes from the scene, but mechanically felt for my jar of water with one hand, whilst I kept my attention fixed upon the wreck.

After looking and dozing for hours, I again fell asleep, and when I awoke it was nearly sundown, and yet the cruel sea was beating over the remains of the hull, which were greatly diminished, and I bethought myself—weak, sick, and feverish as I was—to line the position from my hut before she had wholly disappeared. This I did by moving my head and body slightly till I brought the frame of my southerly window on its southeasterly side to range with a small fir-tree that stood some thirty feet distant, which was in a line with the wreck. I scratched with my thumb-nail a mark upon the window-frame where my eye glanced, and upon the trunk of the tree I picked out a small peculiar branch which aligned upon the wreck. I then, with my right hand, cast some wood that was within my reach upon the fire not far distant, and, over-exerted by all this, fell again into slumber and unconsciousness. It was well into the next day before I regained my senses, and my first glance was for the brig, but not a vestige of her was to be seen, although the ocean was as calm and blue as an inland lake, and nothing but my bearing told me the place where she had gone to pieces.

My wound was a very peculiar one. It will be remembered that the ball had passed completely through my body, breaking no bone, and only injuring my left lung above the heart and just under the shoulder blade. I had not lost much blood, and the doctor, when he left me, gave me strong hopes of recovery, if I could lie perfectly still for at least a week. On this morning I found my fever much better and my appetite returning, and my wound much less painful, but stiff. I crawled from my cot with the greatest care, and renewed my fire from the hidden hot ashes, and soon had a good blaze; for it was chilly during the nights, although I had ample bed-clothing of all kinds heaped about me. I remained in bed for three days more, when I mustered courage to leave my cot and stagger to a chair, where I sat down near the fire. I remained here during the day, and at night crept back again to the bed and closed the shutter of my open window (the door and other window had been closed during all my sickness) and dropped to sleep. The next day I was able to move about quite well, and the orifice of my wound in the back had healed, but the front still discharged and was not closed. I was troubled with a hacking cough, but with the exception of this, on the tenth day, could waddle around, and even into the open air, and procure some of the pure spring water near the hut. Thus I went on till the first of October, getting better and better each day, and making rapid progress towards health. The first excursion I made was towards the shores of the bay, but not a sign of my late comrades in crime could I discover. I also carefully cut upon the fir-tree, with my knife, a notch deep and enduring in the trunk, that lined or ranged upon the place where the wreck had last been seen by my eyes, and at the exact height to have the range pierce the water at the very spot, not more than four or five miles distant. After these two first cares, I began to look about me and see what I had to live upon. My arms were left me, as also was a small bottle of ink that I had brought on shore to keep the daily account of the crew, tides, etc., and several sheets of parchment. These, with my pipe, a little tobacco, quite a quantity of ammunition, my cutlass, a tomahawk, and knife, formed my little store. To be sure I had my wooden cot-bed and plenty of bedding, but this was all. I knew that sweet potatoes had been planted upon the island in several places, and that at least three female and one male goat had also been landed; and as I was fast getting tired of my dry bread and salt provisions, I commenced taking small trips upon the seashore, bringing home eggs, fish, oysters, mussels, etc., and thought at one time that my troubles were all over, and that my wound was healed, but as the orifice closed, I commenced to cough more violently than before, and in the morning my throat was filled with phlegm. And as the middle of the month advanced, I became weaker and weaker, and felt that my end was near, or, if not, it was important that I should guard against all accidents, and for that reason I have written this short memoir of my life and placed it here, to stand as a witness for me, in case of accident or death, that my solitude and wound have brought me to a proper state of mind to view my life with utter abhorrence, and to pray to God in my poor miserable way to forgive me, if it be possible to forgive so great a sinner as I. On this, the 20th of October, 1781, I place this jar in its resting-place, having had the hole to receive it long excavated. I am too weak to even get in and out of my bed, and have spread my clothing upon the floor of my hut, where I can move about easier in the night and get at anything I may want. I close this history here, and I ask all good Christians to pray for my soul should God take me away. It will take me days now in my weak state to cover this up so that the weather and water cannot reach it. I feel that my days are numbered. May the finder of my riches make good use of them, and give largely to the poor, and have masses said for the repose of the blood-stained soul of

THOMAS SUTLAND.

CHAPTER XXV.

Finding of the Sunken Wreck. The Submarine Explosion of the Hull. Recovery of over Ten Millions in Bars of Gold and Silver.

THIS, then, was the history of my predecessor; and his legacy consisted of millions of dollars at the bottom of the sea. He no doubt thought that some of it could be recovered, as he said, "with skill and fortitude;" perhaps by anchoring some boat over the reef, and fishing for it, or in some such lame way as that. He had little idea, when he wrote this eighty years ago, that it would be read by a mortal who had invented a submarine boat, and built it from materials drawn from the very bowels of this very island, and who could descend and examine every part of his famous pirate ship. The reading of this history set my impulsive nature to work at once to acquire the lost treasure. But, to do this, I must first find out where it lay,—its exact locality; and I very much feared that time had effaced the marks that aligned upon the spot, and, if so, I might search for it in vain.

But what was the use of my regaining it? Inside of my brain I was continually answered, "You will escape! you will escape! and with this treasure, added to your stock of pearls and ownership of the island, with its mineral wealth of coal, iron, saltpetre, and sulphur, you will be the richest man in the world. With these industries once developed, your submarine boats multiplied, and pearl oysters procured by thousands, and your island peopled with contented and happy working people, not even the Rothschilds or Barings will be able to compete with you."

Having carefully put aside the manuscript that I had just finished reading, I went on shore to see if I could find any signs of the bearings upon the spot where the "Rover" had formerly gone to pieces. On the window-frame mentioned, I found, although defaced by the weather, a deep cut made in the general direction pointed out, which was no doubt the one referred to; and, encouraged by this, I picked out with my eye several trees of the species referred to in the manuscript, between me and the sea, that I thought might be the one designated; and, having chosen three that seemed likely ones, I went towards them to look for the notch that I ought to find cut in one of their trunks. I found it instantly on the first tree I approached, which had seemed to me the most likely. There it was, plainly marked upon the side of the trunk,— grown over, to be sure, and the tree evidently old and time-worn,—but showing that the wound in its side had been made with deliberation and care, and such as would occur from no natural cause. Being satisfied upon this point, I went back to the hut and placed my eye along the bearings, and found that my sight struck the ocean at some four or five miles distant. This was sufficient for the present; so, getting back to my yacht, I went to bed and to sleep, it being now nearly dusk. In the morning I got under way, and stood out of the bay and rounded Eastern Cape for home, and soon ran up Stillwater Cove, and found everything all right at the Hermitage. I then went to work and made two sheet-iron discs, about three feet in diameter, which I mounted upon iron rods fully fifteen feet in length. I whitewashed one of these with a preparation of lime, and left the other its natural dark color. I then, after caressing, feeding, and attending to my flock of goats and barn-yard fowl, again set out for Mirror Bay, taking these targets with me. Arriving safely, I soon had them on shore, and, after an hour or two of measurements and calculations, had them driven into the ground so as, when in line with each other, to point to the same position on the surface of the ocean, as the old marks were supposed to do, except that they stood clear of all intervening trees or obstructions, and could be seen from the seaward perfectly well. Having these all arranged, I went to work, and, with care and decency, transferred the bones of my predecessor to the hole excavated under the tree, and, reverently placing them within, I said a prayer or two for the repose of his soul, and covered them carefully up. This being done, I made my way back to the Hermitage, and arranged everything about the submarine boat to start early the next day to look for the pirate ship beneath the waves of the ocean.

Bright and early I started down Stillwater Cove in the steam yacht, carrying my treadmill team of goats and all necessary things for my trip. At the mouth of the cove I hauled alongside of the submarine boat lying quietly at anchor, and, leaving the "Fairy" and steam yacht, I went on board, rigged the pendant steps, and started my goat-power propeller, and headed out of Perseverance Bay and around Eastern Cape. The day was a beautiful one; so smooth was the ocean that I did not have to descend beneath it, but held on my way with the manhole wide open; and my goats by this time, by repeated trips, had become quite good sailors and did not seem to mind a little swell any more than old salts would have done. My progress in this clumsy boat was not as fast as in the beautiful and graceful steam yacht; and I was seven hours making the neighborhood of where I expected to find the wreck. I stood on till I obtained a good view of my white and black discs. The one nearer the sea being black, I sailed along, in the first place, till I brought the two in line, and then, the white disc appearing above the black one, I commenced sailing in towards the land, still keeping them on a line, till the former gradually sank down, seemingly, behind the face of the latter, when I stopped the boat, fastened down the manhole, and descended. When I arrived near the bottom I let out my buoy line to the surface, and found that I was in nine fathoms of water, and no sign of a reef of any kind, a firm sandy bottom appearing before me. I therefore still pointed the boat by compass towards the shore, and commenced slowly creeping forward. I had not advanced more than a few hundred yards before the abrupt walls of a solid reef met my view. I ran near to it, and then, by pumping, ascended towards the surface, along its face, till I arrived at the top, which I found by my surface lead line to be not quite three fathoms beneath the water. If any reader should ask how I knew how much a fathom was, I would simply say that every sailor becomes used to measuring off fathoms of rope during his sea life, and finally becomes so skilful as to measure fifty and sixty fathoms of line, and not be but a few inches out of the way, by grasping a piece of rope and stretching it at arm's length across the breast, which, with two inches added, in a man of my stature, should be just six feet, or one fathom, and by this measurement as a standard was my floating surface lead line marked, and it agreed substantially with the foot standard that I had made from my thumb joint, as heretofore described. When I arrived at the top of the reef, I knew in a moment that if I had lived on this side of the island I should in some heavy gales have seen the surf break in this spot; for, by calculation of the tide, which was now nearly at high water, this reef must at times be within eight or nine feet of the surface at dead low water; and in gales of wind I could readily believe that the surf would break over it. Having made all these discoveries and calculations, but with no signs of the wreck, I again descended half way down the nearly perpendicular face of the reef towards the smooth bottom at its base. It was a strange formation, rising abruptly from the bottom of the sea, five or six fathoms, like the walls of a citadel. I saw plainly that a vessel could at one moment, by a cast of the lead, get nine fathoms, and in the very next find herself hard and fast upon the reef, if she drew over eighteen feet of water. Holding myself in equilibrio at about half distance from the surface and the bottom, I moved cautiously along the face of this wall to the eastward, looking for my prize. I went nearly a quarter of a mile in this direction without result, and, turning about, I retraced my steps and made to the westward, feeling sure that at the base of this barrier lay the sunken pirate ship, and that she had never probably passed above its surface; for, having nothing else to do, I had already calculated by means of my Epitome what the state of the tide would have been on the evening of the 23d or 24th of September, 1781, at midnight; and, knowing by the pirate's manuscript that it was probably on one of those nights that the "Rover" was lost, and that an error of a day would only make one hour error in the calculation, I was enabled to find out that it was high water on those days at 5 or 6 P.M., and that the vessel must have struck the reef at very nearly, if not quite, dead low water, when it was within a few feet of the surface, and, being bilged, the rising tide would not, even during the storm, lift her one inch, but only hold her upon the jagged edges, whence she must eventually drop to the tranquil waters at the base. I felt confident that this theory was correct, and that I had only to move along this rocky face till I came to the spot where the vessel had finally fallen back to the bottom of the ocean; and such was the case, for as I was thinking out the problem in my own head, lo! and behold! there lay the wreck nearly beneath my feet, not fifty yards distant.

I approached it with awe, and held myself suspended in the water above it. I then descended and circumnavigated it in all possible directions, and ended by dropping a grapnel near to it, attached to a good strong line ending in a buoy, which I pushed under the tanks, and allowed to ascend to the surface to mark its position for me in the future. I then set my air-boat at work, and soon had enough new air to fill my exhausted tanks, and to rise to the surface and take off the man-hole cover and look about me. I saw that my discs were a little off, and that the wreck lay a little nearer shore and more to the southward than where they pointed. But they had fulfilled their part; they were henceforward useless. I had found the wreck, and had it buoyed so as to be able to again find it, and should I lose it by the buoy being washed away at any time in a storm, the very variation in the discs from the true direction, now known, would show me where to look. I again descended and commenced examining my prize. She lay upon her side, perfectly free from sand or rocks, and had evidently not moved since she sank back from the rocky summit to her cradle at the base. She was terribly beaten and worm-eaten, and both masts had evidently been cut away, as the pirate captain in his manuscript supposed. Her ribs were exposed, and her decks torn up, and innumerable barnacles and shell-fish had fastened upon her timbers. Still falling back into this comparatively tideless and quiet abyss, she had changed very little, I should think, from the day she sank, over eighty years ago. And as she lay I saw that I had another problem to solve, and that was to get at the riches she contained still confined in her hull as in an immense casket. I saw plainly that I should have to blow open the hull to get at what I wanted and expose it. In the meanwhile I was fascinated with the thousand and one old-fashioned shapes about the hull that struck my eye,—the peculiar long brass eighteen pounders, some of which lay beside her, covered with barnacles, but yet showing their shape and general formation; the blunt bows of what the pirate captain had termed a fast-sailing vessel; the comical anchors, and peculiar formation of the decks, that to me, as a sailor, were very interesting. She looked to me more like Noah's ark than the vessel of a civilized nation. How rapidly and almost imperceptibly had we advanced in this science since this tub was called a vessel, fast, strong, and staunch; and how many hours would she have been able to keep in sight a modern clipper-ship, much less overtake her. In comparison to the latter she seemed like a ship's jolly-boat. And so indeed she was, being about 300 tons, as against the 2,000 and 2,500 tons ship of my day and time.

Having satisfied my curiosity and seen that the grapnel to the watch-buoy held all right, I drew in some new air, rose to the surface, and made for Mirror Bay, not over four miles distant. I ran up to the river's mouth near the hut and came to an anchor, and made all snug about the boat, and then, tethering out the goats on the shore, I struck out manfully for home across the island, for I saw plainly that I should have to make Mirror Bay my headquarters for some time to come, and that I must get home and bring together all the powder I possessed, and the steam yacht.

I had a pleasant walk home of about four miles without difficulty, as during the last two years I had several times before crossed the island in this direction, but not often. I put everything to rights at the Hermitage, and then with the steam yacht I visited Eastern Cape, East and West Signal, and Penguin Points, and gathered together all the gunpowder placed there beside the cannon mounted at those stations. I added to this stock nearly all I possessed at the Hermitage before starting, and at the end of two days made my way back to Mirror Bay, stopping at South Cape, and getting all the powder there. Arriving at Mirror River, I found my poor goats glad enough to welcome me back. Putting all the powder I possessed together, I should think that there was perhaps fifty pounds in all. This I put carefully by itself in the deserted hut, and, taking the steam yacht, returned to the Hermitage and my workshop. It was busy days with me now, and I scarcely gave myself time to eat and drink. In my workshop I made a thin cylinder of sheet iron that would contain my fifty pounds of powder, but before bolting it together, and making it water and air-tight, I arranged in the interior two flint locks, exactly like the locks to a gun, only larger. My cylinder was in the shape of a large painter's oil can, which it resembled. Out of the mouth of this can came four strings, two of which would cock the locks, attached inside, and two attached to the triggers would fire them off, or rather release the hammer so that the flint would strike upon a steel plate attached to the side of the interior. These were kept free also from the powder with which the can was to be filled, by placing the latter, when to be exploded, upon its side, with the locks uppermost and clear; the capacity of the can being much greater than the amount of powder to be placed within it, at least one third.

Having my infernal machine all made, and having experimented with the strings leading out of the mouth, and finding that I could cock one or both locks and fire them by pulling the opposite string, I set sail again for Mirror Bay. I had made my infernal machine with two locks simply that, if one did not explode the charge, the other might. Arriving, I went on shore with it and filled it with the powder there stored, taking good care first to see that the hammers of the two locks in the interior were down upon the steel, and not cocked ready for a discharge. Till they were cocked, the powder was as safe in the can as in any other utensil in which it could be stored. And now, being all ready, I went on board the submarine boat for my final test.

I made my way to the wreck, and, descending, was soon balanced opposite the mouth of the main hatch, which was partially open, and large enough to admit ten cans of the size of mine. And now came the dreadful moment in which, under the sea, and far from any helping hand, I must cock these locks within the can, surrounded, as they were, by the powder. It was a supreme moment. I loved my life in spite of its solitude. If anything was wrong in my mechanism, I should in a moment more be blown to atoms, and, if not now, perhaps whilst lowering the machine into the hold of the vessel. I finally mustered up courage to pull upon the string attached to one of the cocks, first placing the can upon its side, and heard it cock inside; but with fear and trembling I slackened the cord that cocked it, and I did not have nerve enough to cock the other, but, forcing in a plug at the orifice, which had already been fitted and had grooves for the four strings, I smeared the whole over with resin that I melted in a lighted candle near me. With a sailor's caution the four strings leading into the can had been nicely coiled upon the tanks ready to pay out of themselves as the can should descend into the hold of the vessel through the open hatchway. Lashed to the outside of the can, I should have said, was a large bar of iron, sufficiently heavy to make it descend in spite of the air it contained. It was with a beating heart that I dropped the whole concern into the water, by a line attached to the middle, and commenced shoving it with my boat hook into the hole in the main hatch where it was to be exploded. During all this time I had the pleasant sensation that if the small cord attached to the trigger should become entangled in any way, and pull with any strain, the charge would be exploded, and I should be blown to atoms. The cold perspiration stood upon my brow, but finally, with a careful but strong push, the can entered the open hatchway and descended quietly to the side of the vessel, where it rested. I immediately cast off from the grapnel that held me near the wreck, and let the submarine boat float away with what little tide there was, paying out, as she drifted, the small line attached to the trigger, a pull upon which, any time during the last fifteen minutes, would have been certain death. As the line began to run out quite freely I began to breathe again; and when several fathoms had run out, so that I knew I was some way distant from the wreck, I began to find relief to my overtaxed brain, and felt that I was again safe, and even as I paid out the small line I thanked God fervently and sincerely. Feeling now sure that I was beyond harm, I commenced to work the pump and to ascend, and at the same time to drift further away, as I did not know what the result of the explosion might be. When I had arrived at as near the surface as the pump would carry me, and felt confident, from the amount of string I had paid out, that I was far enough away to be out of danger, I gathered in all the slack line, and then, with one strong, quick jerk, I proved the practical value of my machine. In one instant the result was conveyed to my ears by a subdued murmur, and the effect by a motion conveyed to the boat as if she had been upon the surface of the ocean instead of beneath it. I was perfectly well aware that, when I pulled the string, the sealed plug in the orifice of the can, through which the string led, would be pulled out, and let in the water; but the same action would also discharge the flint upon the steel inside and cause the explosion at the same instant, before one drop of water could enter, or else I should have fifty pounds of powder wasted. But the muffled roar and the commotion of the water told me that my mechanical ingenuity had not failed me, and that my powder had been exploded if nothing else had been accomplished.

I commenced to descend again and make my way towards the wreck, but was met with such a mass of muddy, stirred-up water, that I was glad to throw a grapnel to the bottom, and lie quietly till it had passed by with the slow motion of the tide. When the water had become again clear, I advanced, and, arriving at last over what had been the hull of the wreck, I looked down upon what might have been considered a vast bird's nest, of which the late timbers of the hull formed the twigs, outline, and shape of the nest, inextricably locked together and interlaced, and in the centre of which appeared, in place of enormous eggs, in relative size to the bird's nest, a large, irregular mass of still yellow and shining metal, although in many places tarnished and dim, that seemed in quantity greater than the mind of man had ever conceived. I descended upon this treasure and hooked up bar after bar, which I placed upon my hanging shelves till I could take no more, and, renewing my air with the air-boat, I made my way to Mirror Bay, and landed my precious freight.

My next work was to bury my treasure where it would be safe, and for this purpose I excavated a large, square hole in the earth near to the ruined hut. Suffice it to say that after many weary trips, extending through months, I had recovered and buried in safety at least ten millions of money, besides having saved six of the brass eighteen-pounders, and a large quantity of copper spikes and bolts. Whilst at this work I came often upon the skulls and bones of the men who had once manned this pirate craft, mixed in with the *débris* of the wreck. Whilst I was engaged in this labor I had to make trips to the Hermitage, and look after my flock, and prepare food for myself, and this was by far the busiest year that I had ever yet had on the island. After carefully covering up my treasure I conveyed all the copper bolts and the old eighteen-pounders to my workshop at the Hermitage, on the steam yacht, where they would be extremely useful to me, as heretofore I had had no brass or copper, and I often felt the need of them in my mechanical arts. I also obtained from the wreck a small quantity of lead in different forms, which was also very acceptable. Having gathered all these riches about me, was I happier than before? I often asked myself this question, and was obliged to answer it in the negative. The very acquisition of this enormous wealth made me impatient of restraint, and more and more determined to solve the problem of my escape. I had the knowledge of being the possessor of this immense amount of money, and at the same time the painful conviction that at present it was worth to me no more than the sand on the seashore.

CHAPTER XXVI.

Chess and backgammon playing. Fortification of the island. Team of white swans. Goats as servants, and opponents in backgammon playing.

YES, here I was, with the wealth of an emperor around me, and not one penny available, in any shape or manner. The acquisition of so much wealth had changed my whole plans; I no longer dared to leave the island, for fear that somebody might discover it during my absence and claim it for their own, and not even allow me to land upon it again, much less become possessed of the immense treasure that I had buried upon it, and which I could only take away by the assistance of others, and they under my own command and discipline. Much as I had bemoaned my fate in being cast on shore, I now feared to leave the island that I had so long hated. The acquisition of riches had brought its usual curse, and from being almost happy and contented I had returned to a state of petulance and nervousness, similar to that which I suffered under during the first two years of my enforced captivity.

The time had come when I felt confident that I could leave the island in some way, in safety, and I did not dare to,—did not dare to run the risk of someone's coming to the island during my temporary absence, and remaining upon it. My common sense told me that I had waited years enough, and seen no one, and that no one would come in my absence, whilst my miserly cupidity and unnatural nervousness told me that it would be just my luck to leave it and return and find it occupied, and all my labors lost; for how could I expect to obtain any legal proceedings to help me, or prove my claim, should such happen. I well knew that in these seas justice was little recognized, and that my return and claims would be scoffed at by any who might have replaced me during my absence. I was at last placed in the woeful predicament of seeing myself aching and longing for freedom, and afraid to accept it should it be offered me. In fact, my cupidity overcame my other desires so greatly that I passed my time at this season in improving all my fortifications, and making myself as strong as possible to resist any attack that might be made upon me. I even went so far as to experiment in the direction of torpedoes, to be placed at the mouth of Stillwater Cove, and in Perseverance Bay and Mirror Bay, to be exploded by electricity should I be attacked. I did not, however, consummate this work, but had it strongly in mind.

I also, at this time, built a small harbor at the mouth of Stillwater Cove, and enclosed the entrance by old stumps and broken limbs of trees, to conceal it, into which I conveyed the submarine boat and steam yacht, when not in use. The "Fairy" I could easily conceal near the Hermitage,—but then, if an enemy ever got as far as this, it would be impossible for me to conceal the sawmill and foundry, and other works below the falls. I was so frightened at this time of being visited, that I built a battery of four guns, to rake the whole of Stillwater Cove, about half a mile below the Hermitage, and to stop the advance of any enemy in that direction. I well knew that, if it was known what wealth I had accumulated, I should stand little chance of ever enjoying it, unless some man-of-war should discover me. It would be very easy for some trader or whaler to dispose of me, and acquire my wealth, and the world never hear of it. Thousands of tragedies occur in these seas of which the world never hears, as I was well aware. My gold and silver I had buried at Mirror Bay, and my pearls I now buried, with care, in a corner of the Hermitage.

At one time I bethought me of making a trip to Easter Island, in my submarine boat, and see if I could not induce the natives, if any, to make me their chief, and if so, to return and, with their aid, build a large vessel, and carry off my treasure to their island, or carry back enough of them to mine to aid me in navigating me to some neutral port, having first fully armed her and taught them seamanship. But if I left the island, I had, in the first place, to run the chance of striking Easter Island, and, having done that, the greater chance of ever again being able to find my own island. This, added to the risk of submarine navigation, which I had before thought over, deterred me. I only seemed to be able to make up my mind to one thing, and that was to protect myself in all possible ways from assault, and to try and study out some way to escape with my treasure in safety.

PLAYING BACKGAMMON WITH THE GOAT.—Page 313.

After some months of this worry, I commenced to return to myself again in a measure, and, having no work of any magnitude on hand, I amused myself in many ways to change the monotony of my existence. Amongst other things that I invented for my amusement were a nice chess-board and men. I had been fond of the game for many years, and I used in the evening to pit myself against an imaginary opponent and set to work. I always played strictly according to rule, and never took a move back or allowed my adversary to do so; and it was amusing to see how hard I tried to beat my other self. I wiled away many weary evening hours in this way, and also with a pack of parchment cards, with which I played solitaire, to my heart's content. But my greatest game, and one in which I took the most interest, was backgammon, which I played with my pet goat. I had here to move for both the goat and myself; but the excitement consisted in the fact of my making him take the dice-box in his mouth and shake out his own dice, so that I really played against somebody in part. I increased this excitement by pitting one goat against the other and making each throw the dice, when I would make the move and reward the winner by a little morsel of sugar, or something of which he was fond. I also managed to make myself quite a serviceable flute, upon which I performed by ear all the old tunes I could remember; and, to preserve them, I marked the notes in a rough style on parchment; but, only knowing their names as A, B, C, etc., I simply marked down these letters to denote any tune, heading it with the name, as "Yankee Doodle," *a, a, b, c, a, a g#, e,—a, a, b, c, a, g#*. I did not know enough about music to keep any other record, but by this method I felt that I could preserve the tunes that I now knew, so as to enjoy them in my old age, if God willed it that I should never escape from this cursed island. At this time I did not know what it was to want for anything: each year my harvests had been greater and greater, and I now enjoyed both apples and pears in great abundance. With saltpetre and salt, and my smoking-house, I was able to preserve all the meat of all kinds that I desired, and my larder and ice-house was overstocked instead of understocked, and I had everything that heart could desire; and yet, since my successful attempt at both the pearl fishery and the sunken treasure, I had been unhappy and discontented. Up to this time I had scarcely seen an hour's sickness since being upon the island.

It was wonderful how good God had been to me; but the delightful climate, and my out-door life and pure water and good wholesome food, had all tended to sustain me; but, with my inventive mind, I did not intend to be caught napping, even in this respect, so to work I went to educate my goats as servants, in case I should be seriously ill. I taught one, after repeated attempts and great attention, to take a little pail that I had made for him, and, at my command, go to the river and fill it with water, and bring it to me at my bedside. After months of teaching, this goat would at last do this duty as well as the best trained servant, and finally I taught him so perfectly that I could get into my bed, touch a little bell that I had made, one tap, when he would immediately look about for his little pail, in whatever part of the Hermitage it might be, and, finding it, march off to the river, fill it with water, and bring it back, and place it always in just the same spot, upon the low sideboard or table, beside my bed. The other pet I taught to bring me a small bag of flour that was kept for that purpose. As I have before said, on a shelf near the bed I had already placed a lamp, spare oil, matches, flint and steel, and all the simple remedies that I had, with candles and a sort of night lamp that I had constructed, with kettle and basin attached. I did not know how soon I might be attacked at any moment with fever and delirium, and I was determined to do all possible beforehand, so as to be able to help myself in my days of necessity; hence my teaching, so that, when too weak to move, I might rely upon my pet goats for good, pure, fresh water and a little food fit for gruel. This teaching was an amusement for me, and not a task; and it was amazing how intelligent these animals became, and how fond I was of them and they of me.

I had noticed that there were upon Mirror Lake, when I had visited it upon several occasions, some magnificent swans, and, having nothing better in my head to do, I made up my mind to capture some of them to transplant to the Hermitage. I made many futile attempts before I could fix upon a plan to secure any of them. I could at times have shot some of them, for they were not very wild, but that was not what I wanted. Finally, after studying their habits, I ascertained exactly where they nestled on shore at night to roost, which was near some stunted trees on the westerly side of the lake. I made myself a large net of strong grass twine and rawhide, nearly forty feet square, with the meshes at least a foot apart, so that the work was not a very hard or laborious one. Armed with this in the daytime, whilst the swans were away, either in the centre of the lake or elsewhere, I visited their resting-place, and attached it to the trees and different uprights, and arranged it so that it could be drawn down and over them at one pull by a cord which I led out into the lake a long distance and buoyed there. Having arranged all my apparatus to suit me, I left it alone for at least a month, not even going near it; when one fine moonlight night I started early, before sundown, across the island to the lake. Hiding myself in the long grass and trees on the border, I saw my friends the swans, about eighteen in number, take their way for their usual roosting-place, and as the light shut down I stripped off my clothing and swam out boldly for the buoy in the lake, which was not over two hundred yards distant from me, but at least four hundred from them. Arriving at it, I grasped the line and gave one tremendous pull with all my strength, and such a flapping of wings and squalling was never heard. All the fowl in the vicinity—and there were large numbers—got on the wing and commenced making night hideous. I hastened ashore, and, slipping on a few clothes, made my way at a run to the place where the net had been sprung. It was as I expected; several of the swans had become entangled, and, having thrust their heads through the large meshes, were endeavoring to make their enormous bodies follow through the same hole, at the same time foolishly threshing about with their wings and trying to fly. It was well that my net was mostly of rawhide, for I found the creatures terribly strong and fierce, but after a fight of over two hours I was in possession of six fine large swans, as beautiful creatures as could well be imagined. All of these I bound with rawhide, with their wings to their sides, and small lashings around their bills, for I found that they could attack with them quite fiercely. After having carefully bound them so that they could not escape, and for further protection drawn the net about them, I made my way home, leaving them where they lay for the night.

The next morning early I appeared on the scene with the canoe, having come around in the steam yacht to the river, which I had ascended as far as practicable, and then taken to the canoe. I soon had my splendid great fellows all in the boat, and thence into the steam yacht in a very short time, when I proceeded leisurely home by the Western Cape, as I wanted to see how that part of my island looked. I saw nothing strange or novel, except the penguins on Penguin Point, who were drawn up as usual in martial array, and I could not help wishing that I had a few brave and devoted sailors with me at this time. How soon we would make the forests of this island echo with the stroke of our axes, and how soon would a strong, staunch vessel arise from the stocks at Rapid River; one that could stand the weather well enough to make the trip with ease to Valparaiso or the Sandwich Islands, or some other civilized place.

Arriving home, I made some arrangements for my new guests, and riveted upon one leg of each a long rawhide rope, which was made fast to a stake on the border of the river. For the first few days there was a great deal of fluttering, sputtering, and squalling, but, being careful not to feed them all this time, I soon brought them to subjection, and in less than a month's time they would eat out of my hand. I then went to work and made a long, light whip, with which I educated them each day for two more months. In the intervals, I was at work in the workshop, and turned out two cylinders, shaped like cigars, about eight feet long and one foot in diameter, made of rolled iron little thicker than common sheet-iron. Upon these, placed distant from each other about six feet, I fitted a nice little deck and an easy, comfortable chair. Having this all completed and arranged, I launched it in Stillwater Cove, and brought it over near the Hermitage. I then made a broad piece of skin that would slip over the head of each swan and rest against the breast, to which was attached a small cord. Putting one of these yokes upon each of my swans, I drove them down to where the boat or car was resting; for I had trained them so that they would obey the whip just as well if not better than a yoke of oxen. Having arrived at the car, I attached them by yokes of two to a central rope attached to the car, and, cracking my whip, set off on a tour of pleasure down Stillwater Cove. Did ever man drive such a car and team before? and yet it was by just such artifices as these that I kept myself from going mad and gave myself excitement and pleasure. No one knows, till they have tried, how easily the birds of the earth are taught. I had often seen a Chinaman make the cormorant fish for him all day long, and make his body of ducks that he was watching as obedient as so many dogs. I knew that my team of swans was of no practical use to me, but it was a pleasure, and that was sufficient. They certainly made a magnificent sight, moving over the quiet, pure waters of Stillwater Cove, and I could not help thinking that, if I should be discovered now, I should be taken for Neptune or some merman of the ocean disporting himself with his favorite team. Having taken a good long ride, I, with a snap of my whip, turned my team about and made towards home. Home! yes, that was the word; it had really become home, and more so than ever since I had become so rich. I could not make up my mind to try and solve the problem which, if solved, would separate me from my island and my riches, and yet I could not go on in this way; I must make up my mind, and that quickly; I must do something; I must choose. If I feared to trust my submarine boat, I could make a catamaran on a large scale, almost exactly on the same plan as the car I was now seated upon, which could not capsize or sink; a life raft, or, better yet, I could construct a boat wholly of iron, with water-tight compartments; but who was to steer whilst I slept,—my goat?—and who was to take care of my island during my absence and keep it safe from all inquisitive eyes? I suppose I should have, perhaps, used up years thinking of this matter, if my attention had not been drawn to other affairs almost as startling as any that had yet befallen me, making me almost believe that I was to be driven crazy by accumulation of wealth which I was not to be allowed ever to enjoy or spend. It occurred to me to make a gunning expedition to Mirror Lake, to obtain some of the wild ducks that were so plenty there. And having now a little lead, I was able to make shot, with which I was more successful than with the steel bullets. With this intention I went to Mirror River in the steam yacht, prepared to stop for a few days and enjoy the sport, and what happened me there I will go on to relate.

CHAPTER XXVII.

Discovery of gold. Turn the stream out of the lake, and build portable engine to separate the gold.

I STARTED with the canoe to the mouth of Stillwater Cove, having first attended to my numerous flocks, and put on board two of my best guns, with some lead bullets and shot, and provisions for some time, and also carrying with me my two inseparable friends, the pet goats. When I arrived, at the mouth of the cove, I entered the concealed harbor, and got out the steam yacht and commenced putting her in order. I soon had a fire built under the boilers, and in an hour's time was all ready to set out. Leaving the canoe behind me, I pushed out of the cove into Perseverance Bay, and made my way to the west about for Mirror Bay. I arrived safely and in good season, and landed to examine my treasure-ground, and found the grass growing over it nicely, and it seemed well concealed. Going on board again, I pointed the yacht up the river towards the lake. I had heretofore always stopped before reaching the latter, for fear of striking the bottom on account of shoal water, but I now made up my mind to proceed in a cautious manner into the lake itself, if possible. I thought that there was water enough if I could keep clear of any boulders or rocks that might possibly be concealed beneath the water. The yacht did not draw over three feet, and I felt confident that she could carry that draft to the lake if she could be kept clear from any unknown obstructions. So I steamed along very carefully and slowly, and often left the helm to rush forward and look over the bows, and, oftener yet, stopped the boat completely and examined ahead before proceeding. In this manner I advanced towards the lake slowly but surely, taking land marks as I went on to enable me to return without injuring my craft by running her upon any submerged danger. At last the lake opened before me, and with a few careful turns of the propeller, I soon floated upon its surface safe and sound. The moment the yacht came in sight, numbers of swans and other fowl commenced to rise from different parts of the lake, and take their departure to more quiet and distant places. I knew, however, that I had not disturbed them greatly, and that they would return during the day, flock after flock. I kept on across the lake to the mouth of a little brook pouring into it, not over fifteen feet wide, and, entering this, I ran on for about a hundred yards, till the water commenced to shoal and to be filled with numerous rocks. Here I moored the yacht carefully to the bank and went on shore. I had no occasion to build any fire or erect any habitation. The steam yacht served me for home, kitchen, bedroom, and parlor, and I had on board of her everything that possibly could be asked for. Tethering out my two pet goats, I took with me two of my guns and quite a lot of ammunition, and the small landing skiff, and made my way back again to the lake. I carried with me also some twelve or fifteen nice decoy ducks, that I had made of wood and dyed with black and red colors, similar to the ducks that frequented the lake. These I anchored at an easy gunshot from the shore, and then, landing, took out my guns and ammunition, which I carefully placed on the sand, and, shouldering the boat, carried it into the bushes near by and concealed it carefully. I then went to work with a hatchet and cut down some of the small cedar and fir trees with which the back part of the shore of sand was lined, and soon had them driven into the sand near the edge of the water, and converted into a blind, from which I could shoot into the flocks of ducks and geese that might come to my decoys without being seen by them. Even whilst I was at work, several flocks were almost willing to alight, hovering over my decoys, but finally departing as they saw me at work. When I had everything to suit me, I retired into my blind and waited for a chance for a good shot. I used to shoot well with a percussion gun in younger days, but I had too little lead now, and too little practice, to try and kill these birds on the wing with a flint-lock gun, and my only chance was to wait till a whole flock settled down, when I intended, by a discharge of one gun whilst they were in the water, and another as they arose, to get as many as possible; and that it may not be thought that I must have had a great stomach for ducks, I would say that I intended to pick and preserve these birds in saltpetre and salt, to use during the winter seasons, and to make of their feathers a nice soft mattress.

I had not long to wait before a small flock settled to my decoys, and, after sailing about a little, became disgusted and made off before I could fire. But after them came a larger lot that settled boldly down, and as I had found out that they would not long remain ignorant of the cheats that had enticed them, I let drive at once into their midst with one gun, and gave them the other as they rose to fly away. As the result of my fire, I counted eleven large ducks dead upon the water and three badly wounded, which I soon despatched by hastening to the shore with my light landing boat and killing them with a boat-hook, and, picking up my dead, brought onto the shore fourteen nice fat ducks. I then drew up my boat and waited for more shots, but the discharge had made the others somewhat wary; but finally my patience was rewarded with two other good shots during the day, in which I bagged three geese and seven more ducks. With this game I made my way back to the yacht, highly pleased with my day's sport. I had noticed, both to-day and in my former trips to the lake, that the species of duck that I had shot were divers, and seemed to get their food by seeking at the bottom of the lake for it, and particularly at this place where the spring water poured into it from this brook or inlet, which evidently arose in a mountain back of me, and, fed by springs, enlarged so as to pour into the lake quite a volume of pure water. As I had to name everything upon the island, I called this brook Singing Water Brook, on account of the low musical murmur that was wafted to my ears from the miniature falls and rocks over which it bounded, gurgled, and found its way, further in the interior, where, from the sound, it evidently was more rapid in its descent from higher ground, but distant enough not to be noisy, but musical, in its progress towards the lake.

I first went to work and picked my whole twenty-one ducks and the three geese, carefully saving all the feathers. I then proceeded to open them preparatory to salting them away in casks which were on board of the yacht, that I had brought for that purpose. I had opened and dressed, I should think, some five or six, when I became curious to know what food they fed upon, and to know if it was to obtain it that they kept diving below the surface. To settle this problem I grasped with my left hand the gizzard of the duck that I had just dressed, and, observing that it was well inflated, I drew my knife across it to expose its contents. It seemed to contain the usual amount of sand and gravel, and a sort of semi-digested food that I was unable to determine as to whether it was fish, flesh, fowl, or good red herring. As I was picking the mass to pieces with my hands, I laid open to view quite a large pebble, fully as large as a pea, that was as yellow as gold. I pounced upon it, for I had seen too much virgin gold in California and Australia not to know it. I had it not one moment in my hand before my sight and its weight convinced me that it was indeed, in verity, a pure golden nugget.

Could it be possible? I had heard before of gold being taken from the crops of chickens bought in Siam and on the coasts of Africa, but I never before had credited the stories; but here before my eyes, in all its unmistakable purity, lay a piece of virgin gold. Then it was this that my ducks were gathering with their other food, mistaking it probably for some kind of grain. To work, therefore, I went upon all of the gizzards of my slain, and my search was rewarded by the finding of seven pieces more, two much larger than the first specimen obtained, fully as large as beans, and the others much smaller. When I had buried my treasure, I had kept out, to have on hand at the Hermitage, several of the ingots of gold and two or three of the bars of silver; why, I do not know, but it was human to have a little amount of gold and silver near at hand,—for what I cannot say; but it was natural, and probably arose from former education and habit. I was not yet perfectly content with the evidences of my senses or the malleability of the metal before me, which I tested by beating one of the pieces with a hammer; but before I would wholly give myself up to the belief that my discovery was really gold, I intended to make a certain and positive test. Stories ran through my head of vessels in olden times, which made voyages to the East Indies, returning home with what they considered gold ore in ballast, which only turned out upon arrival to be simply mica or silica. Whalers also, as I had heard, had given up whole voyages and filled their casks in different parts of the world with worthless earth, thinking that they had become possessed of the wealth of the universe. I was not to be deceived in this manner. I determined, as I have said, to make a final and complete test before I gave myself up to the excitement that would undoubtedly attend my magnificent discovery, if true. For this purpose I left all my ducks and geese, except two for cooking purposes, and made my way as rapidly as possible back to the steam yacht, and, although it was nearly sunset, got under way and started back to the Hermitage with my precious pebbles or nuggets with me. I arrived safely by the aid of a magnificent moon, and ran into Stillwater Cove and up to the Hermitage, when I moored the yacht and went on shore and into my bed; but a restless night I made of it, and early morning saw me at work in the foundry at my proposed test. In the first place I went to work and made a nice pair of balances of steel, with little pans on each side to contain the substance to be weighed. I then went to work and made a mould of iron, by boring out a small oval hole with my steel drills in the face of two pieces of steel, which I hinged together exactly like a bullet mould, only much smaller.

After having everything arranged I set to work and smelted a portion of one of my golden ingots, and whilst in this fused state I moulded several golden bullets in my mould, some ten or twelve in number. I then put the remainder of the gold away, cleaned out the crucible perfectly, and put my nuggets in it and smelted them, and with them made also eleven impressions of my mould in the shape of bullets. I kept these far from the others, so as not to get things mixed. I then placed one of the true bullets of gold in one pan of the balance, and added small clippings of iron in the other pan, till it was exactly balanced. I then took it out and replaced it by one of the bullets made from the metal I had found. The problem was solved,—they were exactly of a weight, or, rather, so nearly so that a minute atom of iron dust added to the pan preserved the balance, for my metal bullet, proved by the very slightest degree to be the heavier. Yes, this was gold,—gold beyond peradventure; but, to satisfy my mind, I weighed and weighed them by one and by twos, and by fours and by fives; always with the same result, scarcely a hair's breadth between them. Practically, they were exact. I knew that no other metal could approach gold in weight so as to deceive me beyond this test. I was living on an island that was a vast gold mine, or at least contained it in large quantities; for it would be impossible for me to have found seven nuggets in a few ducks unless the bottom of the lake was strewed with them at or near the mouth of Singing

Water Brook, which must have poured them into the lake for ages, carrying them along from their first resting-place, the mountain, to the westward from which it took its rise. Convinced that my discovery was real and true, I gave myself up to all manner of day dreams, and it was a week before I made up my mind to return to the lake and explore further. At times I gave up the idea of gathering any of this gold that I now knew lay at the bottom of the lake, and at others the desire to be possessed of it all swayed me also. But, finally, dreaming gave way to my natural temperament, and I made all preparations possible to secure my prize. Should I pen in a portion of the lake opposite the mouth of Singing Water Brook, turn the latter aside, lay bare the bottom of the lake and sift and examine the sand? Alas, this would take great time and pains, and I was afraid also that the water would be forced back, after I had pumped it out, though the sand of which the bottom was formed. Should I lower the outlet of the lake so as to draw off the water in a degree? This was not very feasible, as it was already quite deep, and it would take great time and application to deepen it enough to draw off the water of the lake to any extent. No, I had another plan than this, which I finally decided upon, and that was to use the submarine boat. Having fixed upon the means, I hastened to put them into execution. I made all my preparations, and, taking the submarine boat in tow of the steam yacht, made my way back to Mirror Lake. I had some trouble in getting the former into the lake, but finally succeeded after considerable labor. I had provided myself with some utensils, to pan out the sand with, and also a rocker, that I had built to be placed on shore, and worked by a belt from a driving-wheel of the steam engine of the yacht, which I had attached to it for that purpose only, intending to use it by anchoring the yacht, disconnecting the propeller gear, and leading the belt from the rocker on shore to the engine room of the yacht, and thence to the driving-wheel attached. Let it suffice to say here that during my long stay at Mirror Lake I made weekly trips to the Hermitage and attended to my flocks, but gave up all idea of making butter, and only brought a few of my female goats to this side to give me milk.

Having gotten the submarine boat into the lake, I made a descent in it and examined the bottom. It was almost wholly of pure sand. The water varied from a depth of a few feet near the margin to about three fathoms near the centre. I saw several kinds of fish but none of large size. Having made this examination, I commenced upon the work before me of finding the gold. I went quite near to the mouth of Singing Water Brook, and descended and filled the tops of the tanks with sand from the bottom, failing to find any nuggets with the eye; but I afterwards found several in different trips, but never many or of very large size. Having loaded the boat, I arose to the surface, and beached her near the mouth of the brook, and landed my sand in baskets upon the shore. I then went to work with the pan and washed it in the mouth of the brook, and as the result of this one trip gathered together more gold-dust and small nuggets than I could hold in one hand. This was placer mining with a vengeance, the cream of all mining while it lasts. But I felt that I was going back-handed to work; so the next day, instead of coming on shore with my sand, I took the pan into the submarine boat, and as I pulled it up with a sort of long-handled shovel, washed it then and there in the water of the lake inside the submarine boat; but this again was, during a long day, tiring to my brain, as I had to keep renewing the air by rowing the boat ashore, for it was too shallow to use the air-boat, and I had long ago given up the idea of using the spray-wheel except in case of actual necessity, the air-boat superseding it.

Here I was in the ninth year of my captivity, working hard in my own gold-field. I worked nearly six months of this year, at all spare moments, in this manner, occasionally shovelling sand into the rocker on shore, which I procured from the edges of the lake near the mouth of the brook, just under water, and extracting the gold-dust by means of a belt from the steam yacht. I was quite successful with this method also, but the largest quantity of the dust had evidently been for ages swept into the lake opposite the mouth of Singing Water Brook. I also ascended the brook several times during these months, till it led me to a mountain of some eminence, where it ended in little branches that tumbled down its side.

I got "signs" of gold often,—in fact almost always at the eddies of this brook, and even in its branches,—but never in as large quantities as in the sand at the mouth, although I obtained one very large nugget in the sands of a quiet pool fully half a mile from the lake. I also ascertained that the mountain was composed mostly of quartz,—which miners term the mother of gold,—and all the little pebbles that I picked up in the running brooks were of this description, several of them being prettily marked with little veins of gold. There was no doubt whence the gold came; it had been pouring down from this mountain side in these small trickling streams for centuries, veining the pieces of quartz that contained it till the latter, by friction and water, deposited itself in the shape of sand, and the released gold as dust or nuggets, at the mouth of the brook, having been, perhaps, centuries making the descent from the mountain side to the lake, a distance perhaps of one mile. I knew perfectly well that the mountain contained the inexhaustible mine from which this precious dust escaped, but I also knew that without quicksilver it was beyond my reach to gather it. For in quartz-mining I should need iron stamps, fuel, steam-engine, amalgamator, rocking-table, etc., all of which I could supply, perhaps, except the quicksilver; but this troubled me very little, for I knew that there was more gold at the mouth of the lake than I could gather in perhaps a lifetime, unless I could invent some way to come at it more convenient than the ways that I was now employing. I had often, at the end of a day's work, at this time, nearly as much gold-dust as I could hold in my two hands, much more than one handful, and in value, of which I could only guess, at least $200 to $250. After getting quite a quantity together,—say a week's work,—I used to transport it to the Hermitage, take it to the workshop, smelt it, and preserve the button by burying it within the enclosure of the Hermitage.

I had at the end of some six months become greedy and was not satisfied with my daily gains, but longed to extend my operations. During these months I had not been idle, but had studied upon the problem of how to get at the bottom of the lake. I was thinking about this one day, when nearly half-way between the lake and the mountain side, passing the brook once in a while and looking into its waters for quartz-pebbles marked with gold. At once it struck me, why not turn the brook from the lake towards the sea, in a new direction. I struck my head with my fist to think what a fool I had been for so many months; why, here, even where I stood, was a natural valley on my left, that would convey the water to the sea. I dashed down my pan and worked my way seaward. Why here was even a little mountain brook already tending in that direction, and, following it about two miles, I saw it pierce the sand of the seaside, at least two feet wide, and discharge its tiny current into the ocean. I was crazy with excitement. I dashed back again to the point where I had left my pan, and, picking it up, made for the lake. When I arrived, I went to the inlet and examined it. I felt that I had the whole matter under my thumb, and without much labor, too; for if I should turn the direction of Singing Water Brook so that it would not pour into Mirror Lake, the latter at its outlet would be exactly as low as the bottom, over which a rapid current was now flowing, but which would, by this process, be in one sense brought to the surface; and, as it appeared, I could work upon it, and cut it down, and as I cut it down so would the lake be drawn off, till, if cut little by little, a passage-way which I could timber up to the depth of eighteen feet, all the water of the lake would be drawn off, and the whole bottom exposed to my view, and the golden accumulation of untold ages beneath my feet to pick and choose from. It was feasible, fool that I was, not to have thought of it before. The very next day, armed with axes, tools, and shovels, which I had to make two trips to convey, I found myself at the place on the brook where the natural valley leading towards the sea seemed to meet it, and where a little further on to the seaward I had found the miniature brook, trickling its way to the southward. At the point that I commenced work the brook was not over ten or twelve feet wide, rapid to be sure, but with not a very great descent just at this point. I commenced in the first place by cutting and opening on its southerly bank, towards the sea and into the valley. I did not cut the bank away so as to let the water in yet to its new channel, but worked a little distance from it. For two whole weeks I dug at this, making a good bed for the brook to rush into in its new passage that I intended to give it to the sea. Having this to suit me, I commenced cutting down trees to fall across the brook as it now ran, and these I filled in with pebbles and stones. It was hard work, but at the end of three weeks I had made such a dam across the original brook that I opened the passage for the water into the new one, and kept on strengthening the former till all the water in a day or two bounded down its new course to the sea as if it had always run in that direction. I restrained my curiosity, however, to look for gold in the now dried up bed of the brook, but felled more trees, and put in more stones, and banked up with more earth, till I felt convinced that even in a storm the brook would no longer seek an outlet in the direction of the lake over such a barrier, and with the bed of its new course so well dug out by itself even now, helped as it had been by my labor of two weeks, before allowing it to seek it. Finally I felt my work complete, and, breaking up my camp that I had so long made in the woods, I went back to the lake, looking once in a while into the now empty brook. I should have said that of course, before I undertook this work, I had taken the yacht and submarine boat out of the way,—the submarine boat to its old resting-place at Still Water Cove, and the yacht at anchor in Mirror Bay near the shore. I had been living a hard, rude life in the woods, and had only come out once to go to the Hermitage for food and to attend to my flocks; and I hurried down now to look at the lake, which I knew would be lowered to exactly the former depth of the water at the outlet, some four or five feet. As I came in view of it I saw at once the effects of my work; it looked already woefully shrunken and belittled, but I did not stop to look at it, or for nuggets either. I felt convinced that I had passed many in the bed of the deserted brook, but at present I was intent upon my work of changing the face of nature. In two trips I had all my traps and tools conveyed to the outlet, and it was here that I established my new camp. I had to go to the saw-mill and get some plank, and by the aid of the goats and wagon finally, after bringing them around in the yacht, got them to the outlet where I needed them. I commenced digging in its bed, and the water soon began to pour out, as I did not have to dig a great distance, as the decline was quite sharp. I found that I should not need my boards till I had gotten considerably down, if even then, for my work consisted only in shovelling the bed of the late stream out upon each side and in making a channel lower than the water still remaining in the lake. Suffice it to say that in three months I had the lake drawn off, so as to expose a very large margin of the late bottom. It would take too long to relate how I travelled over these exposed sands and the deserted bed of Singing Water Brook; it will be sufficient to say that my findings were immense, and in the bed of the brook I found several nuggets in what had before been eddies, weighing as high as two or three pounds, as near as I could judge. I soon, however, got tired of tramping over the sand to try and find nuggets by the eye, and arranged to go to work in a more thorough and satisfactory manner. To do this, I left my gold-fields for several months, and went to work at my forge to turn out a portable steam-engine, with a rocker or sand-washer attached. When this was finished I took it, in pieces, to the bed of the lake and erected it on wheels. It was arranged with sections of pipe and hose so as to be placed near the sand that was to be washed, and the water pumped for that purpose from that still remaining in the lake, and which I had left for this very purpose, intending to draw it off and expose more bottom by opening the outlet whenever I should have been over the sands now exposed to view. It was well also that I should have had to make this engine, for the fishes contained in the lake had commenced to die, and the air was impregnated with their effluvia, and the surface was covered with their dead bodies. When I got to work with my rocker and engine it seemed as if the sands were inexhaustible. I often gathered, as far as I could judge, in one day's work, the sum of at least $500, and some days I must have gathered hard upon $1,000, not to mention the nuggets large enough to pick up with my hand, that I was continually coming upon. But at last I got absolutely tired of gathering this golden harvest, and abandoned it for other occupations, having already more than I knew what to do with, and of not one dollar's value to me unless I could escape or be rescued. After my fierce excitement was over in this direction, I returned to the old problem of escape.

CHAPTER XXVIII.

The sea serpent. Attack and capture one of the species, thus putting the question of its existence forever at rest.

It was in my tenth year of captivity that the following adventure occurred to me, which is of such importance to the scientific world, and settles forever such a disputed question, that I cannot forbear to relate it here in the interest of science, and to set at rest all doubts upon this subject forever.

I had started upon one of my trips to the pearl oyster reef in the submarine boat, to obtain some of those bivalves, to convey to the shore for examination. The day was beautiful, and the sky clear and almost without a cloud, with a light air moving from the northwest. I was standing out toward the reef from Perseverance Bay with the manhole open, and all goat power on, when all at once, as I was gazing about the horizon, I saw to leeward of me and off the eastern end of the island, a strange commotion in the regular waves of the ocean. Some animal or fish was evidently splashing the water about into the air in huge quantities. At one time it looked as if the disturbance was caused by porpoises disporting themselves in their native element, and following their leader, in a long string; but I soon saw this was not the case. At another moment it seemed as if a whole fleet of empty barrels had been suddenly left bobbing about in mid-ocean, and then again as if detached quantities of dry seaweed had been floated seaward by the tide, and showed itself as it rose and fell upon the summits of different waves. Whilst the object was taking all these different shapes to my gazing eyes, I was steadily approaching it, having changed the course of the boat, and as I advanced I found that it also was coming towards me, and when within perhaps one half mile, the creature (for it proved to be an animal), suddenly raised its head at least twenty feet above the waves of the ocean, and looked about him in every direction. At once the truth flashed upon me. Here was in verity the sea serpent of which so much has been written and so much doubted. There was no deception; all was too plain before me to deceive a child: but, to prove the matter beyond doubt, I stopped the boat and waited for his near approach. He happened to be heading so that he would naturally pass very near to me, and I got ready to clap down the manhole and descend into the ocean if he made any attack upon me. Just as he was coming along finely towards me, he suddenly plunged beneath the surface and was lost to view. Here was a pretty ending to all my desires to observe him. He had not as yet come near enough for me to describe him, so as to be believed. What should I do? I hated to lose him in this manner, and I felt confident that he had sounded, not on account of perceiving my boat, which he could have scarcely noticed, but, because he was at that moment in the humor or was feeding. Whilst I was uttering useless regrets at having lost him, and making up my mind whether or not to descend myself and try to find him, I was disturbed by a loud splash astern of where I was looking, and, facing about, I looked into the eyes of the horrible creature, not forty yards distant from me.

He did not, however, seem to notice me in the least, but to clap down the manhole cover and descend was with me the work of a moment, for I knew too little of his habits to trust him. I have perhaps before in this narrative stated that, when beneath the surface of the water, all fishes and animals seemed not to take the slightest notice of me; either taking my boat for a submarine rock, or else for a creature like themselves; why it was so, I, of course, cannot say, but that such was the fact I can aver. I had often put my hand down into the water upon the back of quite large fish, when beneath the surface, and it was not till they were touched that they seemed to know that anything out of the ordinary was happening. I had been fully as near the sea serpent as I desired, and descended for safety; his horrible eyes and face haunting me as I fell slowly towards the bottom. Having arrived to within ten or twelve feet, I checked the boat, intending to wait a reasonable time for his lordship to depart, and then to rise to the surface and go on my way rejoicing that he had not injured me; but I had not remained more than five minutes in my position before I saw a sight that frightened me more than meeting this creature on the surface; for, glancing about towards the bottom, my eyes fell upon the serpent making his descent from above, and moving along slowly on the bottom, evidently seeking for his prey. His horrible head passed within at least ten feet of the boat, of which he seemed to take not the slightest notice. As it passed from my view it was followed by the body, at least one hundred feet in length, and as large around as a common-sized flour barrel. I was too startled to move, but kept the boat quietly in position till the whole body passed slowly out of sight. As the tail went by me, my first impulse was to get out of the way, and ascend to the surface, and start for home; my next was to remain where I was and see what would happen. Sitting down, I thought the whole matter over. My solitary existence had given me an inordinate appetite for excitement. I wanted something to stir my stagnant blood, something to call into action all my physical and mental powers. You who have never been cut off from the rest of mankind cannot credit this thirst for something new, something moving, something strange. The daily conversation, the crowded streets, the incidents of life, feed this desire and keep it satisfied; but when there is nothing of this kind, the mind and body both ache to fill the void produced. Add to this such a temperament as mine, and it can be understood that, just saved from an attack from this unknown monster, I determined to attack him, and, if possible, capture him. I don't know why I should have brought myself to this conclusion, or why I should risk my life, but such is man. From a state of fear I entered into one of fierce excitement, and made every preparation to attack the danger I had just escaped.

I had always with me in the boat, two strong, sharp harpoons with long, seasoned, wooden staffs, in complete order, and also a lance and knife. To the harpoons was attached a raw-hide rope, some fifty fathoms in length, and with this I made up my mind to strike the serpent if I could get the chance. To the end of the raw-hide rope, I attached a wooden buoy, and, thus armed, I started the goats, and headed the boat in the direction the monster had taken but a few moments before, and in such a leisurely manner. I had not gone far before I saw the end of his tail coming in view, as he lay stretched upon the sandy bottom. I lowered the boat till I floated about eight feet above the hidden form, and, plucking up my courage, steered forward over him, with his huge body for a guide. As I arrived near his head I stopped the goats, and let the boat drift, the tide luckily being in the direction that I desired to go, that is, what there was of it, which was very little. As the head came slowly into view, I saw that the monster was engaged in quietly crunching in his horrible jaws a fish of some size, that he had evidently just caught, and, upon which his attention seemed to be fixed. The moment was propitious, and, as the boat slowly drifted, not eight feet over the head of the terrible creature, I stood with the harpoon in my hand, and deliberately drove it downward with all my might through his head, just abaft the eyes.

I did not stop to see the effect of my blow, but immediately tumbled into the water, as fast as possible, several of the large stones that I used on the shelves for ballast, so as to ascend at once towards the surface, casting overboard at the same time the line attached to the harpoon, with the buoy at the end. Relieved of the ballast, the boat commenced to ascend instantly and rapidly, but none too soon, for, as it was rushing towards the surface, just below me came the sweep of the creature's terrible tail in its death agony. If I had been struck with it, it would inevitably have capsized my boat, and perhaps have killed me, or, at least, left me to swim ashore to the island, distant some miles, or else be drowned; but, luckily, the blow missed me; the ascent of the boat was so rapid, the very moment I kicked and threw over some of the ballast. Having risen as near the surface as possible, I rigged my pump and ascended still further, and then, setting up my tripod and shipping my air-boat, I soon had air enough to rise completely above the surface, and to open the manhole and look about me. Of course, my first glance was to discover my buoy. Yes; there it lay, not fifty yards from me, without any motion, except what it received from the waves upon which it floated. I could hardly credit that at the other end lay the sea monster, transfixed through the brain with my trusty harpoon; but such, I felt sure, was the case. The mark had been too near and quiet for me to fail, and I had with my own eyes seen the iron driven in up to the staff through the centre of its head. I longed to find out the state of affairs, but did not dare to descend for fear of being caught in the folds of the dying monster. I steered for the floating buoy, and, getting hold of it, by means of a boat-hook thrust out of the manhole, I pulled it towards me, and gathered in all the slack line, till I could feel that I was pulling direct upon the harpoon. No vibration came to me through it, and I could slightly raise the weight evidently attached to the other end, but I was afraid of possibly drawing out the harpoon, so I did not attempt much in this direction; but, being assured that the creature was dead, I finally mustered up courage to descend and look at him. As I came near the bottom, I stopped the boat and advanced in the direction that the line from the buoy trended in. Yes, there he was, dead as a door-nail; but his whole body, that had so lately been stretched along the bottom, was coiled up and around the staff of the harpoon, which had pinned the head to the ocean's bed. I came near enough to see that the creature was really dead, and then, rising to the surface, I made all haste for Stillwater Cove. Arriving, I got up steam on the yacht, and made all haste back to the buoy, towing the submarine boat behind me. When I got upon the ground, I descended in the submarine boat, and, by means of ropes, and pulling and hauling in each direction, I got the body of the serpent somewhat straightened out and the head clear. Around the neck I fastened a good, strong, rawhide rope and attached the buoy rope to it. I then, at a distance of some thirty or forty feet from the head, lashed to the back of the creature my air-boat, to sustain that part somewhat, so that it would not drag upon the bottom. I then arose to the surface and went on board of the yacht, and took the buoy rope to the balance-wheel in the engine-room, and hove the head of the monster nearly to the surface; the water sustaining it, so that it was not very heavy. I trusted to my air-boat to help sustain the remainder of the body, and, thus accoutred, with the submarine boat towing far astern out of the way, I headed slowly for Stillwater Cove, towing my prey behind me. When I arrived at the opening of the cove I drew the carcase as far as possible, by means of the steam yacht, on to the sandy seashore, where the tide would leave it out of water when it receded. I then liberated my goats, and moored the boat in the harbor near by, and, taking my pets on board, after anchoring the serpent safely, steamed towards the Hermitage, where I landed them, and took on board some empty barrels and knives, hatchets, and saws, to dissect my sea monster. When I arrived back the sea had already fallen so as to leave the head and at least twenty feet of the body high and dry. After the tide had wholly gone down, I measured the monster, and these were the dimensions. Taking my measure of a fathom as a standard, the creature was twenty-two and one-half fathoms long, and, at its largest girth—about two fathoms below the neck—over one fathom and a quarter in circumference. It is difficult to describe the monster, but I will try. The head was at least eight feet long, and the extent to which the mouth could be opened over six feet; the gullet was small; the teeth numerous, but small; the nostrils large and prominent; the eyes fully six inches in diameter, and with an expression that, even now that the creature was dead, I could not stand when I looked into them. In the stomach I found only small pieces of different kind of fishes, and, by the smallness of the teeth and gullet, I am inclined to believe that the creature is naturally quite harmless, like most of the mighty animals of the earth,—as the sperm whale, elephant, etc., which never attack anyone unless disturbed. Beyond the head, and, for a distance of some ten feet, grew a sort of mane, formed of pendant tissues of flesh some five or six feet in length, exactly like those to be found on the sides of the mouth of the Mississippi cat-fish or smaller horn-pout. Towards the tail, and some distance from it, was an adipose fin, that was at least a foot high and fifteen feet long. The skin of the creature was of a mottled greenish hue, rough, and discolored, something the color of the shell of a very young crab, and at least a good quarter of an inch in thickness. Having taken all the dimensions of the monster, I went to work and cut off his head, and left it purposely where the fishes, lobsters, etc., would feed upon it at high water, so as to in time preserve its skeleton when all the bones were completely articulated. The remainder of the body I skinned in sections, at different times, and was glad to roll the rest of the body into the current of Stillwater Cove, to be carried out to sea.

THE SEA SERPENT.—Page 347.

I have enough on hand, at the time of writing this, to prove to any one that I have both seen and captured the veritable sea serpent; for, as I sit in the Hermitage, the whole skull, with jaws, teeth, and part of the vertebræ attached, is hung up near me, and below it a circular piece, nearly four feet long, of the hide of the animal at its greatest girth. The frontal bone of the skull, which is not very thick, is broken where the harpoon iron entered and caused immediate death. With this exception the whole specimen is in complete order; and I have also a sketch of the animal drawn upon parchment, from actual life, taken by myself before he was at all mutilated or cut up.

I hope that this truthful, consistent, and convincing recital will close forever this mooted question; for there is a sea serpent, and I have been able to capture and preserve one of his species.

CHAPTER XXIX.

Make a Balloon and Flying Machine, in which I make a Successful Ascension.

My thoughts turned wholly now upon means of defending my vast treasures in case of invasion, and devising ways of escape from the island. As to the former, I overhauled all my artillery at the different points, increased my stock of gunpowder, and had each cannon well supplied with ammunition. I also perfected my battery at Stillwater Cove, and kept the armament on the walls of the Hermitage in excellent order. Not content with this, I went to work in the foundry and turned out several cylinders, similar to the one I had exploded the sunken wreck with, which I fitted with flint and steel, ready to be filled with powder; in short, a species of torpedo, which I had fully determined to take into the submarine boat and explode beneath the bottom of any hostile vessel that should dare to attack me, so much had the acquisition of vast riches changed my disposition. I felt that any vessel approaching and anchoring would be at my mercy; for in the night-time I could approach her, wherever she might be anchored, unknown to anyone, and, attaching one of my infernal machines, send her to the bottom with all on board. I do not say that I should have done this, but I was prepared for all emergencies, and determined to defend my treasure to the last. For means of escape I turned my attention to ballooning,—a subject which I had thought much about, but heretofore had done nothing in that direction. For several years I had been quietly gathering in all the dried pods of milkweed, floss, or silk that I could find,—and large spaces of the island were covered with it,—determined at some time to weave me some kind of cloth or silk from its fibre. I now commenced seriously upon this work, and took hold of it in earnest. It would take too long to relate how many changes I had to make in my loom, which I built of cast-iron, to be moved by water-power, before I could get it to work at all; but I had the theory all correct, and it was only practice that I needed to make cloth. The machine for spinning the floss into threads took me the longest time, but I finally accomplished it. After a while, and with many failures, I commenced to turn out from my loom a sort of cloth, about a yard wide, which was very strong, flexible, and light, but of an uneven surface, on account of the irregularity in the size of my threads, and fuzzy, like coarse flannel; but for strength and practical use I found the material all that could be desired; and, having tested it, I set carding and spinning wheels to work daily to procure thread for my loom. After making some hundred yards of this cloth, I stopped all the operations to experiment in another direction. In my boyhood I had seen balloon-ascensions made by filling the bag with a gas, created by pouring sulphuric acid upon iron or steel filings in this manner: Several old hogsheads were brought upon the field where the ascension was to take place, and into each of them was poured a quantity of iron filings, scraps, etc., and upon this was poured sulphuric acid; the casks were then headed up, and through a small orifice the gas engendered was led by a pipe from each to the balloon, which was thus inflated. If I could make this gas and successfully inflate a small balloon, it would then be time enough for me to advance with my clothmaking for a large one. I easily ascertained from my book how to make sulphuric acid. And this is how I did it: I got together a quantity of sulphur or brimstone, and setting fire to it in a closed vessel, with just enough draught for it to burn, I led the fumes into a closed vessel of water through a short funnel, where, combining with the water, I had at once sulphuric acid. To test this I tackled my friends the dog-sharks, in Stillwater Cove, and obtained several bladders, very thin and light, just suited for my purpose, which I blew up with atmospheric air, and allowed to dry perfectly in the sun. When they were in proper condition I placed in one of my porcelain jars a few handfuls of iron and steel filings, and poured upon it some of the sulphuric acid that I had made, and then lashed the neck of the bladder to the orifice of the jar. I watched my experiment with subdued excitement. I felt sure that I was right in theory; would the thing work in practice? I had yet to see. After leaving the bladder on for a considerable time, I drew a string around it perfectly tight so that no gas could escape and released it from the jar. With fear and trepidation I loosed my hold upon it, and in one moment it shot up into the sky like a rocket till it was nearly beyond my sight, when it disappeared in a northeasterly direction before a strong wind that was blowing. I was as pleased as a boy with his first toy-balloon, and, like a child, I let off several of these bladders as fast as filled with gas, perfectly fascinated to see them ascend and then disappear in the blue ether.

Here was a means at once of sending up daily messengers to all parts of the world, stating the latitude and longitude of the island, and asking for rescue. Aye, but there was the rub; without my treasure how gladly would I have seized upon this method of letting my captivity be known, but with it I had become a coward. I wanted to escape, and did not dare to ask anyone to aid me. The knowledge that I could ask was, of course, a satisfaction, but as yet I did not dare to risk it, and put the matter on one side for further meditation at some future day. Finding that my theory about the gas was correct, I went to work again upon my clothmaking, and worked hard at it nearly six months, when I had sufficient quantity for my purpose, which was to make a balloon of large enough size to make an ascension in myself. I did not have any foolhardy idea of leaving the island in a balloon and landing I knew not where, but I was determined to make a series of experiments in several directions, that had been running through my head for years before, and to see what they were worth. In the first place I went to work and made a balloon, in the shape of an immense cigar, of the cloth that I had manufactured, which was some thirty feet long, and ten feet in diameter. My theory was this. In all balloon ascensions navigators heretofore had only been able to fill a sack with gas, and to ascend into the air, and descend by allowing the same to escape, in other words, to have but little control of the machine except to ascend and descend, and this in a limited degree. I had often noticed that, in the severest storms, seabirds would remain poised in the air without moving a wing, facing the wind, and yet not recede before it, but by a slight motion of the wings, not up and down or a stroke, but a sort of elevation of the body, dart dead to windward against it. I had also noticed that, if a tin plate was thrown into the air against a strong wind, it would often, if at the right angle, increase its speed greatly after leaving the hand, and dart into the wind's eye with extreme velocity. Hence I thought that a balloon could be made to tack in the air exactly as a boat tacks in the water, except that the motion of tacking should be perpendicular instead of horizontal. Suppose that a balloon, cigar-shaped like mine, was poised in air at an altitude of one thousand feet, and that at each end of the car was arranged a light but large horizontal flat surface, exactly like a barn door laid upon the ground, with its hinges attached to the car. To advance against the wind why not elevate the one in front and depress the one in rear to the right angle, or till they were filled as we should say of sails, and then advance into the wind's eye, increasing at the same time the elevation, as the tin plate is forced forward; and, having made a tack upward and forward, why not elevate the rear screen and depress the front one, and descend towards the earth at an angle, still eating our way to windward, and when near the surface reverse the action and mount again heavenward, but still to windward. Besides this, why should not my balloon be filled with gas till it would lift myself, the screens, the car, and all its apparatus *within one or two pounds.* That is to say, to have just enough gas in the balloon, not to raise the apparatus, but to so nearly raise it that another person, if present, could lift the whole in his hand; practically to reduce the weight of my body to that of a good sized duck; then with small wings, not immense cumbersome ones, the same size that would raise a duck, I ought to be able to raise myself, and sail in the air. Could it be done?

After I had made my balloon bag I covered all the cloth and the seams with a fine varnish that I made from the resinous trees of the island. This part of my task caused me little trouble. Having finished it I went to work upon my car and its appurtenances, which I made almost wholly of small cane, very strong but very light. I made also two immense screens or fans, which I fastened to either end, so that they could be elevated or depressed, and covered the light framework with cloth. Underneath the centre of my car was hung vertically a propeller, also made of cane, and the blades covered with cloth, and on each side a fan wheel some six feet in circumference and two wide. The shaft of these fan wheels and propeller was brought into the car, and, by a series of bevelled gear made of the lightest iron possible, was connected with a treadmill for one of my goats, motion upon which would give over five hundred revolutions per minute to the fan wheels and propeller. In this car I also fixed a jar of iron filings and a bottle of sulphuric acid to make gas, if necessary, to replace that which would in time leak out of the balloon if long inflated. I also provided the machine with sand ballast in case I should need it to keep up the equilibrium in case the gas should escape faster than I expected, when I could keep my elevation by discharging it. After this was all arranged, the next thing was to make the experiment.

I have always thought that great advancement has been made in all the arts of navigating the ocean on account of the ease and safety with which experiments can be made, but to experiment in the air one must go into the air, and if the theory does not work in practice, down he comes, perhaps a corpse, on to the hard earth, whilst a capsize in the ocean in experimenting is nothing. Now I had made up my mind to go up in this machine, if possible, but I had also made up my mind that I would go over the water and not over the land, so that if anything did not work, I should only take a cold bath and nothing more; besides, by my theory, I need not go high, and could keep a few feet above the surface of the sea, and if disaster occurred I could swim ashore. I put my goat daily upon his treadmill and worked my machine theoretically till I was satisfied with it. I then made myself a nice life preserver of fish bladders, and put into the car some few provisions and water. The next task was to launch myself properly into space without any disaster. To enable me to do this I went to the mouth of Stillwater Cove and erected a sort of wharf from the shore out into the water at nearly high tide, about four feet wide, upon which I could rest my car with the fan wheels hanging over each side and the propeller clear underneath, the wharf not being planked, but consisting of a few uprights and cross pieces only.

I carried here all my utensils for making gas and had everything prepared for a start. I needed in the first place a day with but little wind, but what there was to be from the southward so as to blow me off into Perseverance Bay when I should start. After some waiting, such a day came and I hastened to take advantage of it. In the first place I took the canoe in tow of the yacht, and anchored it nearly a mile from shore in the direction that the wind blew, so as to be able, perhaps, to reach it if I should find myself too far from land in case of disaster. I then returned and went to work filling my balloon with gas. This I did on shore, till I had sufficient in the balloon to make it steady, when I conveyed it over the car upon the wharf, where I attached it by its numerous cords, and then connected it again with the orifice of the pipe that was supplying the gas. I had before in a rude balance ascertained my own weight in sand-bags, and these I had in the car to represent myself. I put the goat on the treadmill, all harnessed in, ready to start at a moment's notice, and in fact I did start him before the balloon was very buoyant, to see if everything was working right. I walked about the car, lifting it once in a while to see how buoyant it was. I should have said that the propeller had been changed from my first idea, as had the paddles. The former was so arranged as to work vertically, and motion from it ought to force me into the air, whilst the latter were arranged in the form of two lateral propellers, I having bethought myself in season that a revolving wheel in the air would not force me in any direction, whilst a propeller would. The time finally came when the car and all its appurtenances weighed only a few ounces in my hand, in fact nearly ready to take flight of itself. I then cut off the gas and placed myself in the car and commenced quietly emptying over the side the sand bags that represented my own weight; and these being exhausted, I boldly threw over at once two bags weighing nearly or fully twenty-five pounds each, as I was determined to start clear and rapidly from my resting place, knowing that I could easily descend by letting out a very little gas. The effect was instantaneous, and I arose rapidly and commenced floating slowly out over Perseverance Bay; but I had no desire to go high, and I opened the throttle valve at the very moment the balloon started, and at the height of about one hundred feet it was already commencing to slowly descend, which I allowed it to do, till it was about twenty-five feet above the water, when I threw out of gear the lateral propellers and started the goat; the effect was instantaneous in checking the descent, and the vertical propeller was forcing me upward with magnificent speed, in fact I found myself quite too high for comfort before I bethought myself of stopping the goat, which being done I commenced again to descend, but quite leisurely, being very evenly balanced in the air. When I came near the water, I set the vertical propeller again to work and arose heavenward. All this time I was drifting slowly out seaward over Perseverance Bay, and I thought it time to try my lateral propellers; so, setting the gear at once by a handset, I put on all goat power, being at a distance of some fifty feet above the water, as near as I could judge. Everything worked admirably, and I saw that I was rapidly increasing my speed seaward. When I descended too near the ocean I put on the vertical propeller, but I noticed that the lateral ones sustained me as well as forced me forward. I soon ran past the place where the "Fairy" was anchored, and I had now to try my last experiment. By this time I had become at ease in my car, and began to feel as safe and secure as in the submarine boat. By stopping one of the lateral propellers I soon had my balloon turned round and facing the wind, which was at this elevation and out to sea, rather more than I had reckoned upon. As the point of the cigar-shaped balloon came to the wind, I put on the vertical propeller and ascended higher than I had ever yet been, and then, depressing the forward screen and elevating the rear one, I made a dive in a slanting direction towards the ocean; and here I had like to have been shipwrecked, for my car commenced descending with such rapidity that I had scarcely time to reverse the action before I was in the ocean, but happily, by starting the vertical propeller I saved myself, and found the car going just as rapidly upwards.

I had solved the problem. *I was tacking to windward in the air.* I was utilizing the action that causes a boomerang to take the seemingly erratic course it does through space. Having tacked a few times I stopped in mid-air, and, as I had evidently lost some little gas, threw over a small amount of sand, till I sailed again almost in equilibrio. I then put on all the speed of my lateral propellers, and found that I could stem the wind, and that I was approaching the shore. By the action of either one propeller or the other I could change the direction of the car at will, and was enabled to hover over the very wharf whence I started, and to land upon it with a shock no greater than sitting down upon a hard chair.

I then let the gas escape from the balloon, and released my little goat, who had been my mainstay through all this perilous adventure. I had made a more successful ascension than had ever before been made in the world, and if I could replace my goat-power by some other—such as a caloric engine, or some method of compressed air—I should have a vehicle worthy of the nineteenth century. Of course it would not do to have an engine, however small, fed with coal, or I should inevitably have an explosion. At the present I felt that the goat power must do me; and, even if he should fail, my weight was also so nearly that of a few ounces or pounds that I could not fall hard, or with much velocity, even if he should from some reason refuse to work, or some of my machinery give way. The only thing that I feared was the tacking business; this I considered dangerous, with the crude appliances that I had, and I made up my mind not to be tipped out into the ocean, and therefore took them off the car, making up my mind that I would not make an ascension when there was more wind than I could head against with the lateral propellors, and, furthermore, now I had tested the machine, there was no need of my going off the island, over the sea, but I was free to sail all over the land, and if a storm of wind should arise, in which my crude car would be unmanageable, I had only to descend, and walk home.

I may as well say here, that I often afterwards enjoyed myself in the air, floating over my own island, and that I never met with the slightest accident, of any kind; but I could not utilize my discovery enough to dare to attempt an ocean voyage with it. It was a pretty plaything, and would make my fortune if amongst civilized people; but I have no objection to both my submarine boat and balloon becoming public property, as far as I am concerned, I having enough actual wealth, in solid metal, to enable me to enjoy everything in this life worth enjoying.

If this manuscript ever comes to the hands of any one, they can go ahead and manufacture without infringing upon my patent-rights; but should they make an immense fortune, as they are sure to do, why then they can remember the inventor, if they choose; if God wills it that I should ever be where any of my fellow-men can help me, or I them. By my series of experiments in ballooning I had exhausted all my inventions for escape, and I still returned to one of two things: To let the world know of my distress by sending the news by balloons, or else escape myself, in my steam yacht, or life raft, and run the risk of finding the island occupied upon my return, and myself debarred from my treasures and ownership. Between these two I felt that it was time for me to choose, definitely and speedily.

CHAPTER XXX.

The manuscript sent forth.

PERSEVERANCE ISLAND, SOUTH PACIFIC,

January, 1877.

I HAVE decided. I am no longer in doubt. My mind is fully made up as to the course I must take, and that it is of no use for me to remain upon this island fretting my life away. I must escape, I must have companionship, and I must choose. Each method presented to my mind has its advantages, and I have long been in doubt which to adopt: but the struggle is ended; I have fully made up my mind, and shall not swerve from it. If I should try to escape I have the following methods open to me: First, the submarine boat. If I should decide to use that method, I should, in the first place, have to build a much larger one, with room for provisions and bed; and, being larger, it would be propelled much slower by goat power, for I could not utilize a steam-engine on account of the oxygen it would eat up, and the necessary space that would be needed for fuel. Now to build another, and larger boat, would take time and patience, and would be practically useless when built; so I dismissed this from my mind. The one I now had was too small to carry provisions for myself and goats, enough to last any great length of time; and the whole fabric was too crude to trust myself in for a voyage of any length, supposing, even, that I could carry in it sufficient food to sustain life. There was one principle, however, in the submarine boat that I hated to give up, and that was the perfect safety from storms on the surface: these I could escape at all times,— and, again, I should never lose in the night-time what I made in the day. There would be no drifting back, before the wind, whilst I was asleep, but by descending from the surface at night I should rest peacefully till morning, subject only to the slow drift of any ocean current that I might encounter. In stormy weather also I could always keep on my way in perfect calm, beneath the surface, without resistance of any kind except the friction of the water. These points were strongly in my favor; but I could not see any way to utilize them. One great impediment would be the want of air. If I should have to remain below the surface for any length of time beyond a few hours, I should have to keep to work preparing and introducing new air. Then, if my steering apparatus should get out of order, it would be difficult to repair it, and if my goats should die, or become sick, I should be utterly without any means of locomotion, and liable to be left drifting about in mid-ocean till death ended my troubles. No; after long and anxious consultation with myself, I was forced to give up all idea of using my submarine boat, and, having so decided, put it wholly and completely out of my mind, and did not allow myself to think of it again in connection with my escape. This gave my mind relief to concentrate itself upon the second means of escape, namely, the steam yacht.

Here I was again puzzled. There was a great deal in its favor. I should, of course, have to sleep, and during my sleep I should go to leeward, before the wind, without reckoning of where I should bring up. I felt that I could stop this drifting, to a degree, by making a sort of bag of canvas, to be submerged in the ocean to a certain depth to which the yacht could be anchored, so to speak, during the night. She would, of course, still drift, but not one-quarter as much as she would without it. Such an anchor was often used successfully, as I well knew, in larger vessels, in gales of wind, to keep them head to sea, and to prevent them drifting so rapidly to leeward before the blast as they would without it. If I should risk this drifting I might also be exposed to all kinds of weather and gales of wind to which my little boat was hardly equal. I felt confident that she would not be safe in a heavy seaway, and, if the machinery should break down, I should be reduced to sails alone, which I could only handle in the daytime, and which, in any sudden squall, might cause my being capsized for want of assistance in taking them in. No; I knew the risk was too great. I might never see land for months, if at all, if my machinery should give out so as to compel me to use sails, which would often become unmanageable by myself alone. No, I must give this idea up; and I did so.

I next turned my thoughts to a catamaran boat, or life raft,—something upon hollow cylinders, that could not capsize, and upon which I should feel sure of being safe, as far as any fear I might have of the ocean. This seemed more feasible than anything yet,—slow, to be sure, but more safe than any of the foregoing. I had here the danger of being washed off such a raft, the discomforts of being forced to go without fire during any gale of wind, and to be utterly unable to advance, with any great speed, towards my place of destination, unless the wind should be, by chance, favorable. By this third method I should, in reality, be exposed upon an open raft to the winds of heaven, for how long a time God only knew. That I should suffer infinitely I felt certain. I was too old not to see plainly just what I should have to go through with to put to sea in such a vessel. I knew that it had been done, and that just such rafts had crossed the Atlantic after many weary days of passage, and others had started that were called life rafts,—and believed so to be both by practical and scientific men, who had examined them before their departure,—which had never been heard of again. No, I would not trust myself to the mercies of the sea in this manner, and exchange my pleasant island for its dangers.

My last chance of escape was by my flying-machine, and the many things in its favor tempted me greatly, and at one time I thought that they had overcome in my mind the danger. I could easily construct one of these machines, that would take into the air both myself, my two goats, provisions, spare sulphuric acid and steel filings to make new gas, and if my machinery would work I could escape in safety, I felt convinced. I could, as I have said, make new gas, even when on my voyage; and if I should use up all my sand-bags, and needed more ballast, I had only to let down a bucket into the ocean, attached to a long line, and pull up as much water as I might need to overcome the buoyancy of any new gas I might make. I might, also, if a favorable wind should commence, fly like a bird towards the continent of South America. But, on the other hand, if a gale should arise, I might, if one of my fragile propellers should become broken, be hurled before the blast till I floated above the vast ocean far beyond the reach of mortal aid. If I dared trust my machinery this would be the way I should make my attempt; but I did not feel that I had the right to risk my life in this manner, or by any of the above methods, till I had exhausted all means of making the outside world come to me. Therefore, after due and serious consideration, I made up my mind firmly not to try to escape by any of the above plans, or by any means, till I had tried the other alternative.

This decision having once been firmly made, I felt that more than half my task was already done; for it was this shilly-shallying that was undoing me. Anything was better than to waste my life in this useless wavering. What good to me was all my wealth unless I could utilize it? and to do so I must run some risks, and the quicker I undertook them the quicker I should be put out of my pain and misery if my plans were to be successful, and the more years I should have to enjoy my princely revenues. I could not better affairs by any act of mine. It was all in the hands of God, and I might as well now, as at any time, give myself up to what He might order for the best.

Having thus made up my mind to let my position be known to the outside world, and to ask for assistance and aid, I had next to settle upon the best plan. If I should send up, daily, one or more small balloons, with a piece of parchment attached, giving the latitude and longitude of the island and asking for rescue, I ran several risks. In the first place, I was well aware that in these days, on board steamers, with passengers especially, anything and everything was thought of to pass away an idle hour, and that albatrosses, when caught, were fitted out often with letters and legends tied to their feet; that, in sport, bottles were often thrown overboard containing fables and yarns of shipwreck and disaster, and I was very much afraid that, if one of my balloons should be picked up, it would be taken as a hoax, as the first thing would be to examine the chart, and no island would be found to exist where I now write these lines.

Besides, if anybody should pick up one of my balloons, which at sea was improbable, it would, I fear, be taken little account of. For, although I might send up hundreds, the chance of their falling into the water so as to be seen by any vessel, in the daytime, near enough to be distinguished from a nautilus, was extremely and infinitesimally small. No, I had little hope in this direction. On the other hand, should they reach land, the chart would show that there was no known land in the direction specified, and the whole thing would be taken as a hoax from the next neighboring town, and I felt sure no attention would be paid to it. And if any of them landed on the coast of South America, as was possible, and even probable, the English language, in which they would be written, would be so much Greek to the natives. On the other hand, should one of them be picked up by a vessel, and search made for the island, what guarantee had I that I would be allowed to preserve my treasure?

No! I felt that small balloons would be of little use to me, and, in fact, might do more harm than good. What should I do to prove that I was in earnest; that there was such an island, and that I was upon it, in person; and that I needed help and assistance, which I could repay? Why, I felt convinced, by writing a history of all my sorrows, troubles, and tribulations, that would bear upon its face the impress of truth, would carry conviction to any mind that would read it, and would prove to the intellect of any one that it was not *fiction*, but truth, in all its majesty, never to be mistaken for the former.

This, I felt, was the only way to reach out towards a rescue, and it is for this purpose that all that has been herein set down has been penned. Having made my mind up firmly to this, I have written all the above, to be launched into space. Let me beg that my story may be believed, and that I may be rescued; let me ask of you, who find this, by God's grace, to weigh each word and sentence, and feel that you are reading no romance. I shall attach this to a balloon of size, so as to float long in the air, and to attract attention, if ever observed by any one, both by the strangeness of its make and these parchment sheets upon which I have written.

And now let me proclaim to the world the following,—for if this manuscript ever does come into the hands of anyone who intends to seek me out, let all that is contained therein be perfectly understood:—

PROCLAMATION.

In the name of God, Amen.—Be it known to all men, that I, William Anderson, a citizen of the United States of America, do here solemnly declare that I am the discoverer, and at this present the occupant, of an island in the South Pacific Ocean, which I have named Perseverance Island, and that said island lies in the latitude of 42° 21' S., and longitude 119° 11' 15" W. of Greenwich. That I was cast on shore, and miraculously saved by the goodness of God, on Nov. 10, 1865, and that I claim as my own, in the name of the United States, all this hitherto unknown island as my property, belonging to me and my heirs forever; and, inasmuch as I have discovered upon and about this island immense treasures, as recited in a narrative hereto annexed, I ask, demand, and pray for the protection of the United States, and hope that it will be deemed both fitting and proper to dispatch a man-of-war to protect me, for which assistance I am fully ready and capable of reimbursing the government for any outlay; and further, let it be well understood that I, the aforesaid William Anderson, will resist to the death any encroachment upon my property, by whomsoever made; and that for the protection of myself, my treasure, and my island, it is hereby plainly stated, all manner of instruments of defence have been made by me, the said William Anderson, and that the harbors of the island are strewed with torpedoes, and that it is highly dangerous to attempt to land upon any part of the island without intercourse with, and consent of, myself. And that there may be no mistake, and that I may know that if any that approach have seen this proclamation, and acknowledge my just claims and pity my long years of solitude and suffering, I issue the following set of signals, to be by them used in token of amity and that they come to me as friends, otherwise they will be treated as enemies; and although my wealth is great, as herein related, it is believed that pity for my sufferings will touch the heart of any in the civilized world, and I do look most for succor and comfort from the ships of war of the United States of America.

The signals to be made by any vessel approaching the island, which would be in safety, and rules for anchorage, etc., are the following, and must be strictly observed:—

If in the daytime, the vessel, if a steamer, will stand in to the mouth of Mirror Bay till the two iron discs on the mainland are in line, or nearly so, when she will anchor, in six fathoms of water, and then fire three guns, two from the starboard side, one from the port side, and then run up the colors of her nation to the mizzen peak. A sailing vessel will follow these orders except that greater license will be granted her in coming to in a line with the two discs.

If a vessel makes the island in the night-time, she will heave to, or stand off and on, and not attempt to approach, by boat or otherwise, at her peril, till the morning; keeping up, during the night, a red signal lantern at the fore, and firing one gun; when, in the morning, she can stand in under the rule preceding this, for daytime. Having anchored and signalled, the same will be answered by the occupant of the island by two guns from South Cape, when a boat can then come on shore, containing three persons, one officer and two seamen, who, if unarmed, will be allowed to land, and, if honest and true men, as is to be hoped, remuneration for all their trouble in seeking me out will be freely granted. But let it be distinctly understood that all my treasures, of both gold, silver, and pearls, are no longer hidden in the places described in my narrative, but have been removed, and carefully re-hidden, and that an attempt to take my life and possess one's self of my treasures will be futile, for their burying-place will never be known; and I shall resist all aggression with all my might and strength, and, if need be, give up my life in defending my treasure, that I have watched over for so many years.

In my lonely, solitude, with none but the hand of the ever-present Providence spread over to protect me, I sign the above proclamation as my will and desire.

WILLIAM ANDERSON.

PERSEVERANCE ISLAND, South Pacific, Jan. 10, 1877.

And now I have done. I am about to cast this manuscript to the winds of heaven, to be conveyed hence to where God shall think best. Let me beg that the subject-matter of the "Good Luck" may be published in the London newspapers, when attention may be brought to the case, and the old society may send for me, and believe in me much quicker than the outside world will.

I know but little French, but, to still further protect this manuscript I add these few lines, from what remains to me in memory, of the sailor's French that I once picked up, in Havre, in years gone by, so that this may not be thrown carelessly away if it falls into the hands of any who can speak that lingo.

AVIS.

Ne jetez pas cette papier; c'est écrit en Anglais et est DE GRAND IMPORTANCE. Faites rendre en Français, et vous trouverai une vraie historie d'or et de l'argent trouvé par moi sur une isle dans l'océan Pacific.

I have no more to add. I have finished my story with regret. I am tying this manuscript together, and inflating the balloon that is to carry it where God wills.

I will believe in His justice, and await in patience His reply to my many prayers.

WILLIAM ANDERSON.

THE MANUSCRIPT COMMITTED TO THE WINDS.—PAGE 372.]

L'ENVOI.

It may be interesting to call to the attention of those whose eyes it may have escaped, the following that appeared in the *New York Herald* of June 16, 1880:—

"In addition to our account of the wonderful story and succor of William Anderson, from his Pacific Island, with all his treasures, and his arrival at this port in the U. S. S. S. Tallapoosa, published in our last evening's edition, we have to state that, at a late hour, it was ascertained that this remarkable personage, who appears in excellent good health and spirits, will at once sail

by one of the Cunarders for London to confer with his associates there, who were the originators of the "Good Luck" scheme. He states that, having no relatives, he shall, without doubt, expend the larger portion of his immense wealth for charitable purposes, and that it is very probable he may return to Perseverance Island, with a colony, there to end his days."

Lightning Source UK Ltd.
Milton Keynes UK
UKHW010939270722
406450UK00002B/420